THE SLATE QUARRIES
OF PEMBROKESHIRE

The Slate Quarries of Pembrokeshire

ALUN JOHN RICHARDS

ISBN: 0-86381-484-0

Cover design: Alan Jones

First published in 1998 by Gwasg Carreg Gwalch,
12 Iard yr Orsaf, Llanrwst, Wales LL26 0EH
☎ (01492) 642031
Printed and published in Wales.

Contents

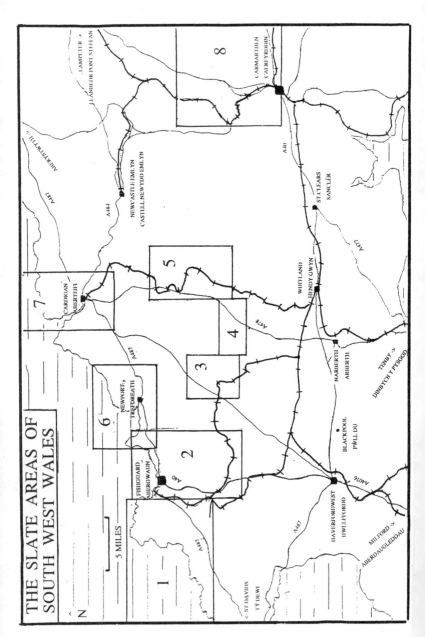

THE SLATE AREAS OF SOUTH WEST WALES

5 MILES

N

ST DAVIDS
TY DEWI

FISHGUARD
ABERGWAUN

NEWPORT
TREFDRAETH

CARDIGAN
ABERTEIFI

ABERYSTWYTH →

LAMPETER
LLANBEDR PONT STEFFAN

NEWCASTLE EMLYN
CASTELL NEWYDD EMLYN

CARMARTHEN
CAERFYRDDIN

ST CLEARS
SANCLÊR

WHITLAND
HENDY GWYN

NARBERTH
ARBERTH

TENBY →
DINBYCH Y PYSGOD

BLACKPOOL
PWLL DU

HAVERFORDWEST
HWLFFORDD

MILFORD →
ABERDAUGLEDDAU

A487
A40
A478
A40
A477
A4076
A40

1
2
3
4
5
6
7
8

Introduction

The south west of Wales is not thought of as a slate producing region yet prior to the industry's great 18th and 19th century expansion, which made Caernarfonshire and Meirionnydd slatemakers to the world, Pembrokeshire's output rivalled that of any of the northern Welsh counties.

North of the Landsker, that imaginary line running across Pembrokeshire eastward from St Bride's Bay dividing the Welsh speaking north from the English speaking south, the geology differs from much of the rest of South Wales. The Ordovician rock forms part of a volcanically influenced band sweeping down from north and mid Wales, in which geological action of heat and pressure has metamorphosed some of the rock into slate giving rise to numerous workable outcrops. From this an industry developed which brought some measure of relative prosperity to barren coasts and uplands.

Whilst the 'Green' slate from the Eastern Cleddau area, became a sought-after product, the traditional 'Blue' slate was not renowned for its quality. Naturally those marketing this product, attempting to sell quarries or to float companies, disagreed, comparing it favourably with north Wales material, often supporting their claims with pseudo-technical jargon. In fact much was highly pyritous, causing rapid degradation, the rotting of roofing timbers and promoting the growth of lichen. Much also split unequally, lost colour and 'shelled' (i.e. flaked). This was particularly true of slate from the coastal quarries which generally could only survive on a roof if 'torched' with mortar.

Although none equalled the best Gwynedd product, a number of quarries did turn out a slate which was certainly better and more durable than say, the Silurian slate of north east Wales.

Almost all the numerous quarries were tiny, some so trifling that it is doubtful if they served more than the occasional needs of the farm or estate on which they lay. Others were worked by Slaters only when they had to find covering for a roof in the vicinity. Some were sporadically worked by a partnership or a handful of men. Just a few had a permanent workforce and a regular output. Even the largest, Rosebush, in its brief heyday, only produced in a year what either Penrhyn or Dinorwig could make in a fortnight.

When the industry in Wales was at its half million ton peak, at the end of the 19th century, the region's 6000 tons was almost insignificant. However, it must not be forgotten that to those who devoted their lives wresting a meagre livelihood from the recalcitrant rock, it was far from insignificant.

Regrettably, with so much small and informal working there is a dearth of documentation which must result in any account being unbalanced and incomplete as well as being an inadequate tribute to those who worked in the industry.

A more fitting memorial is provided by the many roofs, floors, windowsills, gravestones and other artifacts which have so long outlasted the men who created them.

AJR 1998

Quarry Visits

Those quarries which have appreciable or notable remains are starred in the Area Indexes, the number of stars, up to 3 indicating the extent or interest of those remains.

If visiting remember –

All quarries are on private ground and permission must first be obtained, not only to enter a site but also to cross land to reach it.

All slate quarries are dangerous, slippery underfoot, with unstable tips, unguarded precipices and the likelihood of rockfalls.

If tunnels are entered, Hard Hats MUST be worn and adequate lamps carried.

The Products, The Industry, The Transport

The Products

Roofing Slates have always been the Lead Product of the Industry. In early times these were mostly small and crude, ½" or more thick, tapered at the top, and secured by a single oak peg. They were invariably sold in random sizes and set on roofs with the largest on the lowest courses.

By the 18th century these had been almost entirely displaced by rectangles of standardised dimensions. Towards the end of that century sizes increased (eventually up to 26" x 16" and more) as did the number of sizes offered. The north Wales 'Female Nobility' names were not universally used, it being more common to define sizes by dimensions. It is interesting that now, worldwide, sizes are declared in millimetres, but the actual dimensions conform to the inch sizes established in Wales two centuries ago.

By the early 19th century thicknesses had been reduced, 'Bests' being around a sixth of an inch with lower qualities, known variously as 'Seconds' or 'Thirds', or more euphemistically as 'Mediums' or 'Strongs', up to double that thickness. Pricing was usually by the 'Mil' of 1200 (1260 to merchants), but in south Wales some quarries always sold by the 1000, a practice which became universal throughout the industry during the 20th century.

Whatever the size and quality it was regarded as essential that the edges had the rough bevel which occurs on the underside when a slate is trimmed by either a hand or mechanical knife. Although nowadays it would be more economical to produce slates with sawn edges, the market still rejects them.

There remained an outlet for small slates, called variously, Randoms, Odds, Ton Slates or Moss Slates (reflecting the ancient custom of sealing roofs with moss) usually sold by weight. In south Wales uniquely, they were known as Locals and due to a dearth of weighing machines, often sold by count.

Besides the normal argillaceous (Blue) slate some quarries on the upper Eastern Cleddau, worked igneous (Green) slate. From the later 19th century these were mostly sold in Lake District categories, where similar rock is worked. They were thick ($3/8$" upwards), relatively small and sold in mixed sizes grouped by length. Those 14" - 26" long were known as Randoms and up to 14" long as Peggies.

Subsidiary to the making of Roofing slate were Damp Course Slates for which a demand developed during the early 20th century. In 9" and 4½" widths they provided and still provide a useful market for slates whose size or appearance make them unsuitable for roofing purposes. Several south Wales quarries latterly produced them.

Slab which is loosely classed as any product over ½" thick represented an increasingly large proportion of output during the 19th century, particularly in this region. Apart from the crude material sold as building block, Slab products proper were mainly sold in four forms representing increasing 'Added Value';

Common Flagging, split to an approximate thickness, squared off and sold by the ton.

Lotted Slab which was normally planed and offered in specified thicknesses usually from ½" to 2" in ¼" steps, and over 2" in ½" steps in random sizes and sold by the ton in 'Lots' classified according to minimum length and superficial area. In south Wales the terms Slabs and Flags could be interchangeable and were often priced by superficial area.

The third category comprised semi-finished items such as Tombstone blanks for which there was of course a steady trade with Monumental Masons (or 'Sculptors' as they often called themselves), and 6' + x 3' + x 2" Billiards slabs, four being used to make a table bed. Both these could either be sold by weight or by count.

Quarries suitably equipped could also supply fully finished goods such as Windowsills, Lintels, Doorsteps, Dairy Slabs, etc. which were priced by area or length. Other products included Mantelpieces, Urinal sets, Pigsties etc., were priced each. Cisterns were another finished product for which a strong agricultural sale developed during the 19th century to replace those dug from the solid commonly used up until then. They were supplied in sets of five pieces with iron fixings, and like Milk Pans and Pig Troughs, priced by capacity.

From the mid 19th century Ornaments and even Furniture were made out of slate, sometimes Stove Enamelled. [1]

At the opposite end of the scale, blocks and bricks could be made from slate waste. Few south Wales quarries were involved in any of these.

Writing Slates came into considerable demand during the 19th century. These could maximise the return per ton and being mostly sold to Public Bodies were virtually immune from bad debt. However even unframed, they called for substantial investment and high volume if they were to be

[1] From the middle of the 19th century many slate products were offered with enamelled finish. Mostly fireplaces, but also many of the knick-knacks indispensable to the Victorian home. The coating and firing was mainly done by merchants or specialist firms, a disproportionate number of whom were in the mid Cardigan Bay area, there being kilns at Tywyn, Corris, Machynlleth and Aberystwyth. This was due to the local rock accepting a fine surface finish and resisting thermal shock, rather than any special local demand. Very few quarries anywhere did their own enamelling. Its popularity declined rapidly in the 20th century Braich Goch Quarry at Corris being the last to enamel on site, supplying black coated electrical switchboards up to the late 1960's. Several quarries in south west Wales offered an enamelling service, but Dolbadau at Cilgerran was the only one to actually have a kiln.

competitive, since neither of these requirements were normally found in south Wales quarries, almost none were made in the region.

The Industry

It is impossible to define when slate from south west Wales was first dug. Roman slate fragments at Caerleon have been identified as of Pembrokeshire origin but one must suppose that use was being made of an already known vernacular material. Slates were used in Medieval times for the roofing of churches, it being claimed for instance that in the 12th century Whitland Abbey was roofed with Eastern Cleddau material.

By the 16th century there seems to have been an established trade shipping 'Slate Stones' and 'Hilling Stones' to the Bristol Channel and to Ireland. For instance in 1566, 11,000 such 'stones' were sent from Parrog to Bristol.

This is confirmed by the first detailed account we have of slate working in George Owen's 'Description of Pembrokeshire' published in 1603, which also identifies sites and gives a glimpse of the state of the industry. He refers to 'Tiling stones' being found 'about Newport and Dinas, in Cemais in the sea cliffs, and there hence they are sent by water to Haverford, Pembroke and Tenby and to divers parts of Ireland.' Vestiges of quarries in the locations named by him, plus Coedcadw, where he stated, 'the finest sort of these stones are found two miles from the seaside', are still to be seen.

He also referred to these being, 'in assorted sizes and sold by the thousand'. Interesting too is his reference to slates being sold, 'sometimes dear, sometimes cheap, as the plenty and scarcity of those towns do require', indicating that the volatility of demand which so dogged the industry in the

19th century was already a problem. Elsewhere he says that the Pembrokeshire slate is, 'nothing inferior to the high commended slate of Cornwall', suggesting that north Wales was not yet their main competitor.

Reference is also made to a 'Russet stone' and to it being 'Dug very large, three foot and some four foot long, and laid on of that bigness cleaves more rough than the rest, and therefore the lime, taking better hold than between the smooth stone, endures the longer on the house. These stones being laid by a good workman and of a good band, endure well sixty years or more, for there are some houses covered with these stones that scarce any person has seen a tiler on the roof. The best stones of this kind are found at Pant-y-grwndy, Cwm Degwell, Llantood, Henllys and almost every quarry between the river Nevern and the sea.'

This explains the very large slates sometimes seen on old buildings in the area and that the practice of 'torching' roofs with mortar was already established, and indeed that the local slate was not particularly durable. Not that there were many slate roofs in the region, apart from the big estates and a few prosperous farmhouses. In 1811 cottages in Narberth were described as – A mud walling of about 5 feet high, a hipped end, low roofing of straw and a wattle and daub chimney, kept together with hay rope bandages. As late as 1892 it was said that many older cottages still followed this pattern.

With local needs so constrained, the Irish trade was developed during ensuing years and we have accounts that in 1616 40,000 slates went to Ireland, from various ports and in 1639 a total of 36,000 were shipped from Fishguard alone, not far short of the annual total then being sent to Ireland from the whole of Caernarfonshire.

During the 18th century some of the Bristol Channel trade was captured by the Devon and Cornwall quarries, but gravestones, which were then coming into widespread use, identifiable as being from Pembrokeshire, are found in Gower for instance, bearing 18th century dates. There was also trade in roofing materials as the Margam (Near Port Talbot) Estate accounts from the mid century show, e.g. 'By payd John David for the use of Evan Jones in full for 13400 of Pembrokeshire Tylestones. Delivered at Cross Wen Yard towards Repairs of Margam House &c at 8/6 (42.5p) per thousand.'

More ominous, during this century, was the move into the Irish and other markets by the slate diggers in the Caernarfon and Bangor hinterland, presaging the great expansion in Gwynedd. The 1765 founding of Penrhyn quarry at what is now Bethesda, Diffwys at Blaenau Ffestiniog at about the same time, and Dinorwig at Llanberis a little later, began the big producers' domination of the industry. The 1790s saw these quarries hard hit by the duty on coastwise shipments and the wartime increase in sea freight charges, but some were able to take advantage of the lull to improve their infrastructures, the Penrhyn Tramway of 1801 being an outstanding example. Thus when there was a recovery in trade, with prices doubling within the first decade of the new century, their competitive position became even stronger.

Wartime shipbuilding having forced up the price of wood, builders were willing to pay a premium price for larger and thinner slates in order to economise on roof timbering. The big north Wales quarries were able to make such slates and naturally concentrated their efforts on this end of the market.

Since not all rock won was suitable for Bests in large sizes a substantial proportion had to be made into inferior varieties. With their overheads and profits secured on the more valuable product, these big producers could afford to clear their yards of poorer items at prices which might barely cover the slatemakers' wages, and tailored their lists accordingly.

The north Wales Lists determined the prices throughout the industry, so quarries working rock that could only be turned into poor slates in small sizes, which was the position of most of those in the south, found themselves having to sell at prices which even in the largest and most efficient quarries did not cover overheads.

As early as 1836 only five years after the repeal of the tax on coastwise shipments which effectively began Gwynedd's spectacular growth, it was stated that, 'Slates exported from Cardigan sell for half north Wales prices'.

Besides which the trade was increasingly passing into the hands of large merchants, whose order quantities could not be met by the smaller producers. Also even when north Wales quality could be matched, there was a popular perception that slates of Bangor or Porthmadog origin were necessarily better than those from other areas.

Despite these problems which were exacerbated by remoteness from the main English markets, the Pembrokeshire industry did expand during the middle decades of the 19th century, partly due to the explosive population growth in south Wales. Some 6 or 8 sites became relatively substantial industrial units. However increasingly their roofing trade was forced into the lower end of the market.

The one product area where they very much held their own was slab. Many quarries were capable of turning out a product as good as or better than the 'big names' and since slab was judged more by quality than by place of origin, prices obtainable were relatively better than for roofing slate. A stable demand enabled this trade to flourish although the profitability at those quarries dependant on hand sawing must have been doubtful.

As far as roofing slate was concerned, matters improved dramatically in the later 1860s. Prices had climbed steadily through that decade and in the 1870s severe shortages developed. With the north Wales quarries able to sell anything they made, they narrowed the price differential between Firsts and Seconds. Between 1872 and 1876 they advanced the prices of lower grades by 50%. This proved a great spur to activity in the south and during the next few years there were a number of openings and re-openings.

Unfortunately it was all too good to last. The high prices had encouraged both imports and tile making, so the mid 1870s recession put the industry into surplus. In late 1876 the market catastrophically collapsed and by 1884 prices had dived almost to 1860s figures, with even Penrhyn and Dinorwig, offering discounts off prices which they were largely responsible for setting. Prices and quality apart, the dark colour of the Pembrokeshire 'Blue' slate was falling out of favour and it was said in 1882 that it 'Could not command the London or the local market.'

The industry nationally did recover in the 1890s, by which time few quarries in the region had survived as producers of standard roofing slates. Even those eking a living selling Locals at derisory prices found their markets vanishing as more and more outhouses and sheds were being roofed with Galvanised Sheet.

This was by no means the end of the Pembrokeshire slate industry. Although the slab market was contracting well before the end of the 19th century, several quarries notably those at Cilgerran retained a loyal customer base for slab products into the 1930s.

More importantly, some 'Green Slate' quarries on the Eastern Cleddau were able to distance themselves from the fierce competition of conventional slate by offering their product as a premium priced speciality.

This policy served them well into the 1920s and 1930s when fashion having rejected blue/grey slate, more prestigious roofing than the then ubiquitous red tile was being sought. Thus several were able to survive and even prosper in those hard inter-war times. In fact the most successful of these, Gilfach lasted to 1987, its closure effectively bringing to an end, at least for the time being, two millennia of slate quarrying in the southern half of Wales. Now just Cwnc y Derin remains nominally in business and a few sites provide a source of hard core or rough paving.

Finally, mention must be made of the peripheral industries. The region was too small and scattered to give rise to the specialist engineers and suppliers which were a feature where operations were on a larger scale. For these services the quarries depended on general foundries such as Cardigan Engineering for their castings, waterwheels and other machinery and on local blacksmiths and ironmongers, for repairs and supplies.

Local merchants who held stocks, found buyers, arranged shipments and helped to screen the quarries from bad debt were an important part of the industry. Some still survive, sadly now mainly dealing in imported or imitation slates.

Transport

Up to the 18th century virtually all communication with south west Wales was by boat. Even within the region goods and travellers making any journey of more than a few miles went by water. Haverfordwest to Cilgerran, which today takes perhaps half an hour by road entailed a voyage down the Western Cleddau, around the coast to Cardigan and then up the Teifi, which with unfavourable winds could take days.

The road building by Turnpike Trusts from the late 18th century catered for passengers, parcels and mail, but did little to facilitate the carriage of bulk freight. Thus until the coming of the railways in the mid 19th century, the region remained utterly dependent on shipping.

Loadings were made at seaports such as Cardigan, Parrog and Fishguard, at coastal creeks, or at river ports such as Haverfordwest or St Clears.

This trade produced a great tradition of seafaring and shipbuilding. Cardigan for instance, which as the Headport for all the coast from Fishguard to Aberaeron, handled the export of produce and the import of necessities for a wide area of north Pembrokeshire and south Cardiganshire. In 1835 Cardigan had 275 vessels on its shipping register, almost all built there or on nearby creeks and rivers. Such ships served the slate industry well both for export and coastwise to UK destinations.

A few quarries such as those on the Teifi and the Porthgain group had immediate access to navigable water, but most had a long and expensive cartage, which for some meant it could cost as much to move a load of slate to the coast as did the whole production process, and exceed the shipping charges to English, Irish or even the nearer Continental ports.

Some quarries retained a carter on a daily wage, others used hauliers who charged a mileage rate. Smaller quarries would do deals with local farmers, who might be partly paid in kind. This latter practice doubtless accounts for the large quantities of reject slab which still serves as partitions and fencing on many farms near to quarries.

Increasingly from the early 19th century the larger north Wales producers had tramways and narrow gauge railways to reach the coast, slashing their carriage costs to the detriment of those in this region where no area had enough potential to justify such an investment. Although Pembrokeshire would have a number of lines for colliery, military and forestry purposes, the sole slate tramways were the very short-lived Penlan tramway to the Whitland and Cardigan Railway and the sporadically used Abereiddi–Porthgain line.

The arrival of the South Wales Railway to Haverfordwest

and Neyland in the early 1850s, had a minimal impact on the slate trade. A few quarries did use it, reducing cartage distances which offset the high cost of rail freight. It also enabled them to reach inland UK customers, which many northern quarries had long been able to do via the English canal network.

Locally built and registered ships continued to carry slate but increasingly through the 19th century their cargoes were from north Wales ports. For instance in 1863 two Cardigan owned vessels ('Dementia Lass' and 'Andes') were landing slates at Aberaeron, a few miles up the coast from Cardigan, but their cargoes originated at Port Dinorwig on the Menai Strait. In fact coastwise shipping through west Wales ports long outlasted the local slate trade. Haverfordwest and most of the smaller ports survived into the 20th century, St Clears remaining active until the 1920s, Parrog and Carmarthen to the 1930s and it was 1957 before Cardigan Gas Works ceased bringing in coal to their pier.

The one railway which effectively served the slate trade was the Whitland and Taf Vale Railway of 1873. Although two of the quarries it was intended to serve, Penlan (connected by a tramway) and Pencelli (direct incline connection), proved duds, the siding connection to Glogue was vital to that quarry. The 1885 extension to Cardigan brought the line within yards of the Cilgerran quarries, which by this time faced increasing difficulties in using the river due to silting and its use as a tip. The railway enabled some of them and Glogue, to survive into the second quarter of the 20th century. Although none of the several proposed feeder lines from the Eastern Cleddau quarries was ever built, it did offer a marginally shorter cartage than to the GWR.

The Maenclochog Railway, though built almost entirely to directly serve the Rosebush quarry, was not completed until 1878, just when the slate market so disastrously collapsed. It initially only ran for four years, towards the end of which time it actually brought in north Wales slate.

All in all the effects of the railways on the slate industry of this region were mixed. They did enable some inland quarries to expand and replace the coastal units, partially accounting for the eastward migration of the industry during the latter decades of the 19th century.

Unfortunately there was downside. Only those quarries directly or almost directly connected could make economical use of the railways, and then they were in head on competition with the big north Wales producers. Conversely those same big producers could flood the region with their own superior product and cheap imports could also readily be brought in. In addition the railways carried in bricks and cement, wiping out much of the local market for slate block, quoins, sills, lintels and flooring, as well as, making galvanised sheet and other slate substitute items more readily available.

During the early 20th century the steam and later the motor lorry obviated the problems of reaching a port or a railhead. But by the 1930s, better vehicles and the raising of speed limits made all-road delivery possible, accentuating the grip on the market enjoyed both by the large producers and the importers.

Summary of Railway Carrying Slate

South Wales Railway (Later GWR). Opened to Carmarthen 1852, to Haverfordwest 1854 (Broad Gauge to 1872).

Used by several quarries in east Pembrokeshire loading at Narberth Road (Renamed Clynderwen), possibly some use at Haverfordwest by Sealyham. Its extensions to Neyland (New Milford) in 1856 and Fishguard in 1906 had no slate significance.

Maenclochog Railway (Later North Pembrokeshire and Fishguard Railway, afterwards GWR). Opened from a junction west of Clynderwen (GWR) to Rosebush 1876.

Closed 1882. Reopened 1884. Closed 1888. Reopened 1895 (As NP&FR) to Letterston and to Fishguard in 1899. 1917 closed Maenclochog–Letterston, goods only to Maenclochog. Full service restored 1923. Closed to passengers 1937. Trecwn branch opened 1938. Intermittent suspensions during WW2 for military purposes. Closed Clynderwen Junction to Letterston 1949. Closed Letterston to Letterston Junction 1965.

Directly connected to the Rosebush quarry, may have had trifling use by other quarries. Had the extension to Letterson come say 20 years earlier, it might have had a dramatic effect on several quarries in the Puncheston area.

Whitland and Taf Vale Railway (Later Whitland & Cardigan Railway, afterwards GWR). Opened from Taf Vale Junction (Later Cardigan Junction), (West of Whitland GWR) to Glogue 1873, Crymmach 1875, Cardigan 1885. Closed passengers 1962, goods 1963.

Directly connected to Glogue and to the short lived Penlan and Pencelli quarries. Llanglydwen and Crymmach Arms stations were used by some adjacent quarries and there were substantial loadings at Cilgerran station after 1885 by the Cilgerran quarries.

Abergwili Junction – Llandilo Railway, Llanelly Railway & Dock Company. (L & NWR, later LM&SR)
Opened 1864. Probably some slate loadings at Abergwili and possibly Nantgaredig. Closed 1963.

Carmarthen & Cardigan Railway (Later GWR). Opened Carmarthen to Conwil Elvet 1860, Llandyssul 1864 (Broad gauge). From 1866 to 1872 mixed gauge Carmarthen to Pencader Junction (as part of Manchester to Milford Railway) Extended to Newcastle Emlyn 1895. Aberaeron Junction to Aberaeron (Lampeter, Aberayron & Newquay Rly.) 1911.

Closed progressively from 1964, the route from Carmarthen to Green Grove siding for Felinfach Creamery being retained to 1973.

Bronwydd Arms to Cwmdwyfran was reopened 1978 as the Gwili Railway (With plans for an extension to Cynwyl). Also a length of the bed at Henllan, once an important cattle and wool station, is used by the narrow gauge Teifi Valley Railway.

Although the original Prospectus of 1852, refers to 'Lead Mines, Stone, Slate and other Works on or near the proposed line', it proved to have no slate significance. However had the quarries between Llanpumsaint and Pencader fulfilled their mid 19th century expectations it would have been vital to them.

The Methods, The Men
and their Masters

The Methods

Almost all slate in this region was extracted from hillsides or cliffs by methods basically similar to stone quarrying. The only variation being in some cases to divide a high face horizontally into terraces to enable more men to work and to minimise breakage of block by limiting the distance it fell. Where working progressed downwards into a pit, every endeavour was made to access and drain by a cutting or a tunnel, to avoid pumping and uphaulage costs.

With the putative exception of Summerton there was no underground working in Pembrokeshire, tunnels only being cut for drainage or exploration. There is evidence of at least an intention to work underground at Penygraigygigfran north of Carmarthen.

However slate is worked, the basic principle must be the same; to extract blocks of rock, to select those which can be made use of and discard those that cannot. Usable blocks are then reduced to manageable sizes, split and then trimmed to produce thin rectangles for roofing material and thicker and larger rectangles for slab products.

Methods were ably described by George Owen in 1603,

'This stone, being dug in the quarry, is cloven by iron bars to the thickness of a foot or half a foot – and for tile they cleave the same to what thinness they think best.'

The crowbarring and wedging of block from the rock face, was replaced during the 19th century at the larger quarries by blasting with gunpowder. Shot holes being drilled with hand drills or with Jumpers which were weighted rods that were repeatedly jerked to make a boring. Just a few in the region eventually used compressed-air drills.

A 'Plug & Feathers' or a massive mallet were used to prepare suitable blocks for final splitting, which was done by skilful use of a hammer and a thin broad chisel, a process that has never been satisfactorily mechanised.

Roofing slates were then trimmed to rectangles by supporting an edge on a fixed blade, usually attached to a stool and striking it with a knife with an offset handle. From the mid 19th century mechanical trimmers came into use, but few south Wales quarries could afford them. Where they were used they were of the Greaves rotary type which was, and still is the industry standard, but were almost all unpowered, operated by a treadle or pedal.

Slabs were split in the same way as roofing slates, a heroic task where large sizes weighing a quarter of a ton or more were involved. Again Owen referred to this aspect of the industry in 1603,

'– make large mantels for chimneys of one stone, and of three stones the whole frame of a large door, viz., one pillar for every side and one to cover the same either archwise or square at your pleasure.'

Owen may have been referring to a coarse slate when he said that this

'Tuff stone served for stairs as a stone whereon a man may boldly tread without sliding'.

The trimming and squaring off of slab by chiselling was largely replaced in the early 18th century by sawing.

In other regions the usual method of sawing slab was by Sandsaw which was a framesaw, usually two-man, with a plain untoothed blade, the cutting action being produced by wet sand introduced into the kerf. Whilst there is gravestone evidence that such saws may have been used, in south west Wales, toothed hand saws were universally employed. They had a blade about 3' long and 9 " wide with a Tee-bar handle at one end and either a Tee-bar or a vertical handle at the other. Blocks to be cut were apparently held upright with the saw used at about 45° by one man standing and another kneeling. Whilst toothed saws were used elsewhere for detail work such as notching, their use for main cuts seems to have been almost unknown elsewhere in Wales.

Sometimes this handworking was done in the open air without shelter of any kind, but except at the tiniest quarries there were usually open fronted dressing sheds to provide a modicum of shelter.

Although wheelbarrows continued in use well into the 20th century, most movement within quarries was by hand pushed trams generally on 2' gauge track. Where differences in level were involved, some larger quarries used gravity inclines, the downgoing loaded trucks hauling up empties. For upward movement there was some early use of horse whims but several quarries uphauled by steam inclines or by steam cranes. Cefn at Cilgerran and putatively Summerton, had aerial ropeways.

Quarry layouts changed with the coming of mechanical sawing of slab which called for a mill remote from the actual quarrying area in order to be both at a water source and to be well clear of future extraction. Water powered saws had been used in the slate industry from the early 19th century but apart from their presumed use at Summerton in the 1830s, they did not appear in this region much before about 1850. With the enigmatic exception of Summerton, it is inferrable that all were of the standard Greaves pattern, with a fixed circular blade protruding through a slot in a moving table.

Quarries with sawing mills besides deriving the obvious cost advantages from power sawing, could also use planers enabling them to offer smooth surfaced slab which from the mid 19th century, buyers were increasingly demanding. Early slate planers, manufactured by several Caernarfonshire firms, had a powered table, the 6" wide blade being traversed by handwheel. Later versions made by Turner of Newtown were more substantial, could accept a blade 12" wide and had automatic blade traverse. Planing as well as almost doubling the sales value per ton of slab, enabled, by the use of appropriate form tools, grooves, profiled edges etc. to be produced, adding further value to the product.

Although slab became a mainstay product of many quarries in the region, few were large enough to justify the expense of power sawing. Apart from the one or two which used handcranked circular-sawing machines, the rest persevered with the toothed handsaws, all suffering the competitive disadvantage of being unable to offer planed finishes.

Where power was needed for mill drive as well as pumping or haulage, obviously water was the first choice, but the lack of suitable streams meant that in the whole region there were less than a dozen water-wheels and turbines. Few if any having adequate reservoirs.

Thus nearly all the mechanised quarries had to resort to expense of steam. Towards the end of the 19th century some oil engines came into use and one quarry, Glogue eventually had electricity.

The Men

The heading is deliberate, women turned the windlasses and drove the carts of the collieries of Pembrokeshire, women and girls broke up the ore in copper mines and in agriculture women performed menial tasks such as weeding and stone picking. In slate quarrying there was no female labour, even the girls who in the 18th century tended pack horses carrying slate in Caernarfonshire, had no counterpart in this region.

Total numbers were never large, the peak census year of 1871 showed fewer than 170 men in Pembrokeshire describing themselves as slate workers. Even adding non slate-specific occupations such as carter and labourer, it is difficult to substantiate the large workforces which folklore attaches to quarries such as Rosebush and Porthgain.

Although some men originated from other quarrying areas, particularly north Wales, most were drawn from local agriculture. There was never any difficulty in attracting them as north Pembrokeshire was traditionally a desperately poor region. In the 18th century farm labourers might expect to be paid 4d (1.6p) per day for the eight summer months and 3d (1.2p) for the four winter months plus 3 meals and a jug of skimmed milk provided at the farmer's house. The meals would be frugal in the extreme, particularly in the 1790s when times were hard for farmers. In 1797 the usual diet of labourers in Narberth parish was described as – 'Bread and Cheese, Potatoes and Porridge' (a thick flummery made from coarse oatmeal). In the Fishguard area diet was said to be of 'Herrings, Potatoes and Barley Bread'. Meat and butter had occasionally appeared on cottage tables but by the 1790s, price increases had put them quite out of reach and shortly grain would also rise steeply, giving rise to food riots.

By the early 19th century top workers on a lowland farm might get 1/- (5p) per day, but a series of bad harvests kept food prices high and a pair of boots for instance would cost a whole week's wages. Survival depended on having a plot to grow vegetables or keep a cow and on wives obtaining casual work in the fields or helping at harvest, as well as possibly weaving flannel cloth to sell at fairs.

Workers in metal mines did slightly better, but even such skilled men as shipwrights would only take home 1/6 (7.5p) per day. Other than in the coalmines of south Pembrokeshire, no occupation could approach the wages which slate quarrying offered.

For example, in 1825 at Craig y Cwm, Slate Makers were getting a daily rate of 2/6 (12½p), Rockmen 1/8 (8p) and

Labourers 1/4 (6p). At the time a living-in unskilled worker on a hill farm could well receive less than £3.00 a year.

As time went on agricultural wages did increase. By the 1840s a farm labourer could get 4/- (20p) per week plus keep and by the 1880s, a skilled ploughman might get as much as 14/- (70p), although with fewer perks than in the past. There was a lesser increase in quarry wages, but there was still enough of a differential to make the occupation attractive. It was only in the 20th century that slate quarrying came to be regarded as a poorly paid job. For instance in 1913 Teilo Vale's top rate was 4/- (20p) per day, with labourers pay as low as 3/- (15p), only a little above farm workers and well below the average in industry.

The Bargain system, usual elsewhere in Wales was by no means common. Under this system gangs, generally of four men, were each 'let' a section of working face normally for a period of four weeks. They would agree (or be forced to accept!), a rate of payment for the number slates made. Only support artisans and any labourers not paid by rubbish tonnage being on a flat daily rate.

In this region it was not uncommon for the whole workforce to be on daily rates with curiously, Slate Makers who split and trimmed being paid much more than the equally skilled Rockmen who won the rock. Under the Bargain system these jobs tended to be interchangeable, both describing themselves as Rockmen with the term Slate Maker being reserved for makers of Writing Slates.

Even where there was piecework or other output related payments, most workers had a reasonably constant income. Under the Bargain system payments could vary considerably from month to month and the fortunes of gangs differ dramatically. Although the system was jealously defended by the men, it was a constant cause of discontent.

Few quarries were large enough to require tradesmen such as masons and mechanics on their payrolls, it being rare even to employ a smith. Usually a local blacksmith was contracted to take care of the equipment, possibly providing him with a forge on site. He would also, for a fee, sharpen the men's own tools.

Unlike other slate districts, there was little friction between master and man. This was in no way due to any meekness on the part of Pembrokeshire men. Apart from the food riots of the early 19th century, land enclosures at Maenclochog in 1820 provoked a robust response and in 1839, some of the earliest of the Rebecca rioters repeatedly destroyed the toll gate at Efailwen. Steady wages and workforces small enough to directly negotiate with a working proprietor, undoubtedly contributed to this lack of confrontation. There was never a need for a counterpart to the North Wales Quarrymen's Union, nor of any formal employers' combination. Besides which proprietors readily granted time off for hay harvests, funerals, fair days, preaching festivals and so on which were often causes of dispute in big, highly organised quarries elsewhere. More importantly, the practice common elsewhere of employers solving cash-flow problems by withholding wages seems to have been virtually unknown in the region. It is believed that the only major instance of this in Pembrokeshire was at Porthgain in 1879/80, causing the only significant strikes ever to occur in the county.

Wages may have been steady but employment was not, few quarries were continuously worked, so migration from job to job, particularly amongst skilled men, seems to have been accepted as an occupational hazard. Other than in the Cilgerran area it was unusual to see men appear in more than two consecutive parish census'.

This movement created accommodation problems. The larger quarries, notably Porthgain and Rosebush built and let cottages which formed the nuclei of present day villages. Central to Sealyham's great expansion plan of 1877, was the provision of workers' housing. Elsewhere some housing was erected and let by builders.

Some men built their own houses. Some of these, particularly on the uncultivated slopes of the Preseli mountains, being 'Tai Unos' (one night houses). These were built under a tradition that if a rudimentary house could be commenced after nightfall and have a fire lit by dawn, the squatter would have, in a year and a day, title to its occupancy and a permanent dwelling could be erected. He also was entitled to all ground 'within an axe's throw of the door'. This had no legal foundation but was in fact rarely challenged.

Where no houses were available, most quarries were close enough to settlements for lodgings to be obtained. Some men may have temporally at least, slept rough at the workplace but the provision of Barracks commonplace in extractive industries at remote locations elsewhere was unknown.

In contrast too with other areas, work appears to have been less hazardous in this region. Like outdoor workers everywhere, cold and wet would have taken their toll, but the dust-related diseases endemic in areas where most men worked underground or in sawing mills, were comparatively uncommon and there are examples of men working at 70 and even 80 years of age. Lack of underground working, a dearth of machinery, restricted use of explosives and often a more measured pace of work, meant that accidents were fewer than in other slate districts. Only three deaths from accidents have been identified, Cefn in 1898, Teilo Vale in 1912 and Gilfach in 1956, all from rockfalls. Sad though these losses were the fatality rate was clearly well below the industry average and far less than the late 19th century Meirionnydd figure of almost 2 per 1000 p.a.

The Masters

Owing to the actions of a few north Wales proprietors, an opprobrium has become attached to the term Slate Quarry Owner. Few southern Wales owners could be considered grasping, if only because there was precious little to grasp.

Some of the small quarries were worked by farmers as part of their exploitation of their land, others by landowners to supply the needs of their estates. A number were operated commercially, often part-time, by individuals or partnerships.

Of the ones which became large enough to require an employed workforce, the proprietor was usually either a local landowner or a self-made ex-quarry worker. Even when they traded as companies backed by finance from outside the area, a degree of control normally remained in local hands. All of which contributed to the good industrial relations mentioned above.

Only the Abereiddi/Porthgain/Trwynllwyd complex operated over an extended period by 'remote control'. It may be coincidence that this was seemingly the only quarry in the region to have industrial relations problems.

Large or small, overwhelmingly proprietors in this region were honest men attempting to turn honest profits in the risky business of slate quarrying.

At best it was a boom or bust enterprise, with prices oscillating with the state of the economy in general and the building industry in particular, as well as wars, threats of wars and other external factors. Plus, as has been said, most proprietors in this region were locked into the lower end of the roofing slate market, often at artificially depressed prices.

Slab proved a better bet towards the end of the 19th century but to be competitive this called for big outlays to mechanically saw and plane. Costs of these often being inflated by the need to use steam, resulting in most of the mechanised quarries having a Capital to Revenue ratio much above the industry average.

A great brake on investment, apart from lack of money, was the lease system. Whilst at the end of a lease plant might be sold, infrastructure reverted to the landlord, so that it was only freehold quarries such as Glogue and Rosebush that could think long term on non-portable development.

There were other problems too. With the best merchants and agents tied to the big producers, the more marginal quarries often had to deal with customers who were financially unsound frequently resulting in non-payment.

Bad debt apart, up to the end of the 19th century almost all product was sold on three months credit, terms which customers often stretched to six months or more. It was usual to offer 2½% discount for cash against invoice, but this was commonly deducted even when payments were months overdue. Even the general introduction of a 30 days credit period after WW1 failed to appreciably hasten payment and surviving ledgers are full of trifling 'payments on account' of quite large debts.

Besides this, in order to be able to meet orders promptly large stocks had to be held. These could represent large sums of dead money, which had to be disastrously written down when prices fell or demand changed. At the same time quarries' major outgoings were wages which had to be paid out monthly, and carriage which although added to the invoice, still had to be settled promptly. Thus they were in a 'negative cash-flow' situation, the brisker business was, the more money was needed to finance it.

Owning a slate quarry in South West Wales (or almost any where else for that matter) was not a path to wealth.

However there was one very quick and effective path to wealth – by financial manipulation.

A number of companies were floated particularly during the slate mania of the 1860s and 1870s. Spurred by tales of the vast profits being made by the Penrhyns at Bethesda, there was no shortage of investors anxious to put their money into slate. Most quickly found this to be a costly error.

Some were genuine if sadly over-optimistic attempts at quarrying, most were not, being designed to extract money from the pockets of the incautious rather than rock from the ground. Grand Prospectuses were issued 'Guaranteeing' huge dividends, backed by fulsomely favourable opinions from 'Experts'. These would be followed by letters or planted articles in Newspapers or Trade Publications, drawing readers' attention to an 'Outstanding investment opportunity' or to the 'Timeliness of putting money into slate'. Some were quite shameless e.g. One Robert Hunt commented on slate quarrying in 1865, when trade was flat and many well established quarries were struggling, that '50% is the average profit in Wales, with the best 100%'.

Central to all such promotions was the lease. Having obtained this, usually at just the cost of the legal fees, the promoter would sell it to the company he was floating for a large sum. Even when part payment had to be accepted in shares, these could usually be sold before the whole house of cards collapsed.

The 'Mister Big' of such doubtful promotions was John Davies of Newtown who scenting opportunity, moved to Narberth in 1864. Accompanied by Henry Ledgard, a London man, they set out on a twenty year nefarious career. Davies' methods were ably summarised by a letter to the *Mining Journal* from J.F.N. Hewett of Velindre House in March 1865;

I have heard of a case in which a man took a worthless vein, placed on it one whom he dubbed a 'manager', changed the name of the place, caused the quasi manager to write (or wrote for him) a flaming report on it under its new appellation, signing as manager of so and so, (the old designation); and, thereupon starts an office, with a confederate who has some cash and some influence. They take to themselves 4 or 5 friends, kin or whatnot, assess the amount the public is prepared to pay them, and forthwith launch a company. The same course is pursued with another and another concern, nearly all equally hopeless, each 'manager' reporting on the other affair, and many of them mere working men, all but unable to write, and really do not know to what statements they append their names. When once the affair is floated, the directors who are also the promoters, do not care whether it succeeds or not, except insofar as getting their fees or salaries and keeping the work alive until the promoters are paid, or as actually has been the case, until they have got the shares up at a premium, when they sell out, and make a still better thing of it than by merely 'acquiring' the money paid by subscribers, and then the thing collapses suddenly. To my certain knowledge nine or ten such companies have been floated by one man and his confederates, several more are ready to be launched and others are on the stocks.

While John Davies is not named, he is clearly the target as Davies had just bested Hewett for control of the Porthgain quarries. It is amusing to reflect that Hewett's involvement with the Esgern Slate Quarry Company at Esgyrn, less than a year later could have been described in similar terms.

Davies was not always successful, several of his promotions fell to pieces leaving him with dud properties, but overwhelmingly they were not, it is a tribute to his persuasiveness that mugs were still being spruced even after the late 1870s slump.

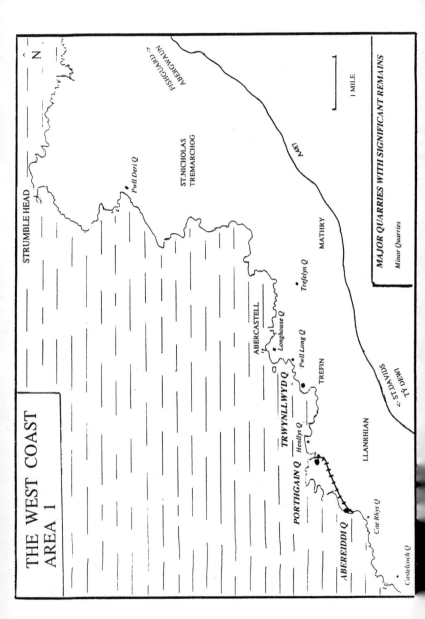

THE WEST COAST
AREA 1

N

STRUMBLE HEAD

FISHGUARD
ABERGWAUN →

Pwll Deri Q

ST.NICHOLAS
TREMARCHOG

ABERCASTELL

Longhouse Q

TRWYNLLWYD Q

Pwll Long Q

TREFIN

MATHRY

Trefelyn Q

PORTHGAIN Q

Henllys Q

ABEREIDDI Q

Cae Rhys Q

LLANRHIAN

← ST.DAVIDS
TY DEWI

Castelcoch Q

MAJOR QUARRIES WITH SIGNIFICANT REMAINS

Minor Quarries

A487

1 MILE

Area 1 The West Coast

Slate was worked at several places on or near the coast between St David's Head and Strumble Head. Although there is little documentary evidence of work prior to the early 19th century, presumably outcrops were exploited from early times. Very much sea-dependant, material was either directly loaded into boats, or carted to the nearest creek. Some product was clearly used in the immediate area, but some went further afield forming part of the trade of tiny ports such as Abercastle.

The only workings to have been developed and mechanised were Abereiddi, Porthgain and Trwynllwyd which for some 50-60 years operated jointly as a substantial if not always successful commercial enterprise. Their combined output ranked them as one of the largest in south west Wales. Taken together their remains are the most extensive in the region and include an external tramway.

```
SM776304  Castellcoch
   794303  Cae Rhys
   795315  Abereiddi     ** (R)
   813325  Porthgain     **
   817328  Henllys
   832329  Trwynllwyd **
   840331  Pwll Llong
   845337  Long House
   864327  Trefelyn
   893384  Pwll Deri
```

ABEREIDDI SM795315
An ancient cliffside quarry loading directly into boats. Undoubtedly well established before 1838 when it was leased by W.J. Ward, E. Williams and J. Jones, who traded as the Barry Island Farm Quarry. All were local men, Jones described himself as a Slater, suggesting he had been

working as a roofer making his own slates. The landowner, Irishman George Le Hunte charged no rent, merely a royalty of 1/10th of the value of sales made. Since they sold almost nothing, he must have been relieved when they surrendered the lease in 1841.

It was immediately re-let to a London syndicate of Benjamin Hill, Robert Norman and John Barclay who commenced serious development here and at Porthgain. In granting a 40 year lease Le Hunte safeguarded himself by stipulating a minimum royalty payment of £50 for the first 5 years and £100 for the next five.

In 1849, having replaced the horsewhim by a vertical lift powered by an 18hp steam engine, erected housing and other buildings and introduced terrace working, the trio were in trouble. A sheriff's order was issued against Barclay who had been working Trwynllwyd independently. The partnership was reformed without him, Trwynllwyd was bought in and a fresh 50 year lease on Abereiddi obtained.

The 1851 census suggests a substantial workforce at the three quarries, there being 58 slate workers living in the locality, only 8 having been born in the parish and of the rest 30 were from north Wales. That census also showed 5 'Railway labourers' indicating that the 3'g railway was then being built to facilitate shipment at the new 100' piers at Porthgain.

In 1855 the enterprise was registered as the Barry Island Slate & Slab Co. Landsales were made from a yard on the railway which also served as a stocking area for seasales as there was restricted stocking space on the Porthgain quayside.

Thereafter their fortunes (and misfortunes) followed those of Porthgain. Production ceased at end of 19th century but some sales from stock continued into the 1900s.

Remains The quarry pit is now open to the sea as after closure a passage was blasted in an attempt to make a harbour. This severed the line of the tramway and now isolates the engine house etc., some dressing sheds and the stonework of the lift. Separately isolated are a few of the contiguous line of about 15 dressing sheds that bordered the tramway. Alongside the line are various buildings including an office and manager's house, a powder house and a forge, below rail level is Abereiddi Row of seven workers cottages, originally let at 10d (4p) per week. The rail formation of the horse-drawn tramway to Porthgain is traceable for part of its length.

CAE RHYS (Porth y Meibion) SM794303
Very small. Documents from 1807 mention slate at Aberpool (Aberpwll?) and Pwllcarog, either or both may be this site. Advertising Locals as well as Sizes 'to order' in 1880.
Remains Quarry face.

CASTELLCOCH SM776304 & 776306
Two tiny cliff workings. Mid 19th century?
Remains Some scarring of cliff.

HENLLYS SM817328
Cliffside working, with difficult landward access, in 1870 repeated advertisements appeared –

HENLLYS SLATE QUARRY
To Masons and Farmers, slates of all sizes may be had from the above quarry. Apply on Bank.

Similar advertisements continued to appear at intervals up to at least 1879, by which time the words 'On moderate terms' were appended and Samuel Hughes was named as Manager.

In January 1890 it was announced that:

'The United Welsh Slate Company Ltd., Porthgain, are now the proprietors of the Henllys Estate and will supply the well-known Henllys slate on the same terms as formerly. Apply to Joseph Hetherwood.'

United apparently did not work it for long.
Remains Traces of excavation, a wall (building?) high up on cliff. Not to be confused with the farm of same name which has some shallow pits at SN113395 and was a much earlier site.

LONG HOUSE SM845337
Tiny working. In 1859 John Harries of Trevine was advertising 'Locals @ 18/- (90p), to cover 27 square yards.' (probably 1000), as well as Countesses and trimmed flags, all for 'Ready money'. There was again advertising in 1879 for Locals, again for 'Ready money'.
Remains Excavation.

PORTHGAIN SM813325
This mainly slab quarry had presumably been worked before the Hill, Norman & Barclay partnership took it in the 1840s, as the 1851 census showed 2 'miners' employed, suggesting that a drainage tunnel was already called for.

A new 25 year lease was obtained in 1855 when the Barry Island Slate & Slab Co. was formed, consolidating this quarry with Abereiddi and Trwynllwyd. William Pritchard, an experienced Caernarfonshire quarryman who had been managing Sealyham quarry, was brought in to take charge.

In 1859 they were extensively advertising their wares in the local press –

'To builders and others, the Barry Island Slate & Slab Company are prepared to sell slates and slabs at the following prices deliverable at the quarry situate between St David's and Fishguard.

Per thousand of 1260

	First Quality	Second Quality
24 x 14	£8. 8. 0 (8.40)	£7. 2. 6 (7.12)
24 x 12	7. 5. 0 (7.25)	5. 17.6 (5.87)
22 x 12	6. 0. 0	5. 0. 0
22 x 11	5. 0. 0	4. 10. 0 (4.50)
20 x 12	4.17.6 (4.87)	4. 0. 0
20 x 10	4.14. 0 (4.70)	3. 15. 0 (3.75)
18 x 10	3.10. 0 (3.50)	2. 12. 6 (2.62)
18 x 9	3. 0. 0	2. 12. 6
16 x 10	2.17. 6 (2.87)	2. 2. 6 (2.12)
15 x 8	2. 5. 0 (2.25)	1. 12. 6 (1.63)
14 x 8	1. 6. 0 (1.30)	1. 2. 0 (1.10)
14 x 7	1. 4. 0 (1.20+	1. 0. 0
13 x 7	1. 0. 0	15.6 (.77)
12 x 7	18. 0 (.90)	14.0 (.70)

Locals to cover from 28 to 33 yards   14. 0
                      25 to 28   12. 6 (.63)

Superior Slabs for Tombs, Headstones, Cisterns etc. from £1.10.0 (£1.50) and upwards per ton.
Flooring Slabs, sawn edges and planed surfaces 22/6 (£1.12) to 25/- (£1.25) per ton.
Mantelpieces, Windowsills etc. made to order.
Apply Mr J. Jack, Porthgain Trevine.'

The range of sized slates (presumably mostly from Abereiddi), was exceptionally large, and one wonders if they actually had 28 varieties available or whether such a comprehensive list was 'window dressing'. The prices were 15%-20% below north Wales lists. Comparison of slab is difficult as elsewhere it was usually sold by area or by the item but the above prices were clearly very much less than the going north Wales rate. No realistic comparison can be made on 'Locals'. It is of interest that the unit of sale for the sized slate was 1260. It was commonplace for the 'Thousand' to comprise 1200 pieces, only sales to merchants being in 1260s.

Obviously the mill which ultimately had 6 saws and 2 planers powered by a 24' water wheel was by now in use.

At the beginning of the next year, 1860, with demand increasing, most producers were upping their prices. However, presumably to stimulate sales their advertised prices were unchanged. In spite of this the company failed later that year.

The preliminary announcement of the Chancery sale offered inter alia, 'the tenant's interest in the valuable machinery and plant' which suggests that it was subject to mortgage. It also stated the 'Refuse from the quarries can be thrown directly into the sea'. If this referred to Porthgain as well as the other two quarries, it suggests that some debris was being trammed out through the original drainage tunnel.

The Sale Particulars included at Porthgain 3 horse whims and a horse pump, a slate yard on the railway, a whim for winding at Trwynllwyd, the steam winder at Abereiddi, and the seven cottages there, as well as the row of seven, Pentop, on the cliff top at Porthgain and the seven near the harbour. The Sale map shows the tunnel running due north out of the pit to emerge in the cliffs. An incline almost parallel to it with a whim at its head. Another whim nearby with possibly a chain incline, both these presumably dealing with rubbish. There are a further 2 whims to the east, one apparently with a vertical haulage to feed the adjacent head of the gravity incline down to the port and the other possibly the pump mentioned in the Particulars. Presumably the workings were now below the level from which the tunnel could drain.

It is of interest that the 1861 Census showed a number of dwellings occupied by quarrymen's wives, presumably the absent husbands being north Wales men who had returned to seek work.

The quarries were reopened in 1862 by two English businessmen, J.F.N. Hewett and A. Grierson. They proposed the erection of a pier, a windmill, workshops and a mill dam at Porthgain. Quite what they did is unclear, for in 1864 their manager Mr Henderson was inviting tenders for the working of Porthgain and Trwynllwyd quarries and their mills (but not Abereiddi?). That year they formed, in conjunction with John Davies, the St Brides United Slate & Slab Co. to run all three quarries. Hewett and Grierson were to have been paid £12,000 in shares for the properties. They did receive some shares, but were outmanoeuvred for directorships by John Davies, who appointed his friend H. Ledgard Managing Director. At first Henderson was retained as manager but by 1866 he had been replaced by William Pierce late of Tal y Sarn quarry north Wales.

They were now pricing Porthgain slab by area, quoting 3/- (15p) per square yard for planed flags, but a mere 1/- (5p) for unplaned. They were selling Locals @ £1 per 1000 and 'Stones' @ 1/- (5p) per load.

They backed their bid for additional finance in 1868 with a report by T. Nicholas late of Dandderwen which promised, 'A large percentage for a small outlay'. Nicholas stated that Abereiddi was being worked on 4 galleries, that 72,000 sized slates were being made per month including 19,000 of 20 x 10s at an alleged cost of £1 19 0 (£1.95) per 1000. (This cost figure could imply that a Bargain system was being operated.) He optimistically asserted that these would sell at £7 and when the 'intended tramway' was completed (rebuilt?) the carriage to Porthgain then costing 2/9 (13.5p) would not exceed 4d (1.6p) or 6d (2½p).

Trwynllwyd, he said, was making the 'best slab known' which could be raised for 20/- (£1) per ton and sold for 30/- (£1.50) to 70/- (£3.50), and carted or boated to Porthgain. Production was stated to be small but could be increased although, 'a very large outlay would be required'.

Porthgain called for £300 to be spent clearing rubbish and '40 yards of extra tunnel for the 3rd gallery', but it could produce 'fair slates and slab of the largest sizes'. He said that slab could be raised and planed for 8/- (40p) per ton and sold for 20/- (£1) to 40/- (£2). The lower selling prices for Porthgain slab is understandable but the huge difference in costs is puzzling and only partly explained by the fact that Trwynllwyd were now using steam for haulage and mill power.

In 1869 they were selling for cash only and threatening defaulters. That October they resolved to wind up.

By this time the Abereiddi railway had been rebuilt and the 16hp Robey engine to power a chain incline from the Porthgain pit had been installed, but in 1874 Messrs. Robey were still trying to obtain payment for the engine from the liquidator!

In 1875, the redoubtable John Davies put together the St Brides Welsh Slate & Slab Co. and having got his hands on the lease, sold it to the new company for a reputed £25,000. London subscribers included E. Williams a wine merchant, W. Ellard who may have been his employee and J.C. Holden a Coal Merchant, typical of the small investors prepared to stake their savings in the then booming slate industry.

That the company expanded operations is undisputed but their reputed payroll of 300 is extremely improbable, it being unlikely that the total for all three quarries ever much exceeded a quarter of that. In fact the 1861, 1871 and 1881 censuses, admittedly all taken at times of minimal activity, respectively showed only 12, 17 and 27 men in slate-related employment living in the parish.

A news item of 1875 spoke of the 'excellent' St Brides slate quarry having been started a few months before with T. Williams as manager and engineer for the three quarries. Due to a poor water supply a 20hp Hazeldines engine was installed to back up the waterwheel at Porthgain mill.

Further quarry openings were planned north east of Abereiddi with tramway connection. This idea may have been the germ of the subsequent Granite workings.

The 1878 collapse of the slate market caused considerable problems. In 1879 the men walked out complaining that they were owed four months wages. Tom Williams had long gone and had been replaced John Fraser. His advertising began to smack of desperation:

SLATES AND SLABS FOR SALE. The St Bride's Slate & Slab Company have on hand one hundred thousand 3rd quality slates ranging in sizes from 10 x 8 to 24 x 14 which they will sell at greatly reduced prices. The 10 x 8 which will cover as much as the ordinary Local slates will be sold at 15/- (75p) per thousand, and the other sizes at equivalent rates in order to make a complete clearance of stock. The above slates when they are set in mortar are exceedingly durable.

Porthgain Flooring slabs at 2/9 (13p) per square yard, planed on 1 side also floors fitted to order at 3/- (15p) per square yard.

50 ton of Trwyn Llwyd slabs planed on both sides of various lengths, breadths and thicknesses, but not exceeding 3 feet in length which will also be sold at reduced rates. The slates can be shipped at Porthgain harbour.

Apply John Fraser, Manager St Brides Quarries, Porthgain Letterston RSO.

Some cash must have been raised as the men did get one month's money and resumed work. But the next year with the three months arrears still outstanding they struck again. The press reported the quarries 'nearly idle', and shortly after that the company failed. It would appear that creditors tried to salvage what they could, advertising in August 1880;

Porthgain Slate Quarries
Clearing stock. Size slates are being sold as Locals. These

slates when laid in mortar are equal to any slates in South Wales. L. Lewis, Manager of Works.

The United Welsh Slate Co. was formed in 1883. All the sponsors, W.E. Griffiths, G.C. Manders, M. Grimaldi, J.A. Green, C. Cronin, E.D.T. West & T.P. Wood being from London. John Davies having claimed the lease by the St Brides default, sold it to the new company for £13,600 cash plus the same amount in shares. His name did not appear on the list of sponsors but a disgruntled investor writing to the press in 1885 alleged that John Davies had 'built the company on the ruins of St Brides'.

Appreciable tonnages of slab were produced, and a larger boiler was installed to improve mill output. Abereiddi's roofing slate contribution tapered off and before the end of the decade its tramway was mapped as disused. They commenced brickmaking, cutting a 150 yard tunnel enabling brick material to be brought out direct to the quayside. They started the Pen Clegyr Granite operation, bought a stone quarry at Solva and a steam ship the 'Maggie Anne'.

By 1891 they had all the appearances of a prosperous, well diversified outfit, advertising in March that year:

THE UNITED WELSH SLATE COMPANY
Granite, Slate slab, Debris, Bricks and Tiles &c, Coal, Oil and Lime Merchants.
This Company owns the harbour at Porthgain and the Trinity Quay at Solva and are now prepared to carry goods of all kinds between London, Manchester, Liverpool, Bristol, Cardiff and Swansea &c and their own depots. A steamer will be run between Bristol and Solva at regular intervals. Goods should be delivered to the care of Messrs. Baker and Butt, Shipping Agents, Bristol.
As the Company own and run steamers to the purposes of their own trade, they are in a position to ensure regular delivery at very advantageous rates.

A constant supply of Granite, Slab, Bricks and excellent House Coal as well as Culm, Lime &c can be obtained at Solva and Porthgain.

Managers and regular staffs of men are always on duty at Porthgain and Solva and the depots are furnished with steam cranes, weighing machines and all appliances for the dealing with coal and other goods rapidly at a moments notice. Ample warehouse accommodation is provided.

All goods are weighed on a machine and a weight note is given. The company also maintains a depot at New Milford for the supply of best steam coal for steamers use.

Orders and enquiries sent to the offices of the company or to either of the Depots receive immediate attention.

James Jamieson, Manager Porthgain

H.W. Williams, Manager Solva.

But in fact they were fast becoming the 'Untied' Welsh Slate Co. In trouble in 1888, the company had been reconstituted by H. Birch, the company secretary, who having got his hands on the lease sold it back for £10,000 plus shares. Trwynllwyd had reverted to its landlord depriving them of their best source of slab. There were several calls for further capital and seven months after the above advertisement appeared they were out of business.

Birch formed the Porthgain Granite, Slate & Brick Co. in 1893 claiming an output of 50,000 bricks per week which an additional big kiln would increase to 80,000. He stated that Abereiddi could produce 20,000 slates per week as well as 50-100 tons of slab from Porthgain.

He appears to have immediately sold out to C. Roberts, A. Harlow and other London investors for a reputed £45,000, and started his own Porthgain Harbour Ltd to develop the harbour.

The PGS&B company, in spite of grandiose plans only

lasted two years and in 1897 the Porthgain Quarries Ltd with M.J. Hennesy as manager was formed to pick up the pieces. By 1900 just 3 men were working on slate at Porthgain and 1 at Abereiddi. The harbour company was consolidated into the quarry company in 1904 and all interests were acquired by the Bristol based Forest of Dean Stone Firms Ltd who concentrated on granite, operating it through its subsidiary United Stone Firms. No slate work was done after about 1910 and following great success with crushed Granite in the 1900's, a succession of companies persisted until the 1930s. Everything is now owned by the villagers themselves.

Remains Most prominent are the bunkers of Porthgain brick from the granite era. Behind them are track beds and several structures including a loco shed, all part of the 1900s Granite operations and unconnected with slate.

At the pit bottom is the row of hoppers which define the later tunnel to the port, earlier tunnels have not been traced. The cutting to the head of the just discernible ropeway incline is on the south rim, the original incline to the north has been quarried away. Nearby are the vestiges of a powder house, a possible engine house and the row of seven cottages, Pentop Terrace, which were occupied up to the late 1940s.

Little is left of the mill, other than the wheelpit which has a lavatory over the tailrace. The slate-lined leat is notable as is the pleasing harbour office. The original harbour cottages were augmented by the later operators who eventually owned 58 dwellings, most of which are still in occupation. The harbour warehouse has been restored and to the east of the harbour are the remains of brick kilns. The port tunnel is now gated.

PWLL DERI SM893384 & 893385

Tiny cliffside workings accessed from land.

Remains Northerly working is on 2 levels. Traces of access tracks.

PWLL LLONG SM840331
Tiny cliffside workings late 19th century?
Remains Scarring of cliff face.

TREFELYN SM864327 & 868326
Small. It was clearly an established working in 1879 when Benjamin Watts of Abercastle advertised:

> A large quantity of Locals of superior quality at moderate price, may now be obtained at the quarry. Sizes made to order.

Watts was placing -similar advertisements up to 1891 closing shortly afterwards.
Remains Two excavations in trees near the river.

TRWYNLLWYD SM832329
Originally a cliffside operation partly worked from boats. The early history is unclear, 1800 has been suggested as the start date but Hewett writing in 1862, claimed that Llanrian church tower was roofed with Trwynllwyd slate in 1786.

It was leased by Barclay of Abereiddi in 1841 who may have commenced horse-whim haulage to make slab at the cliff top, supplementing or supplanting slate making on the beach. Following the sheriffs sale against him in 1849, it was taken by the Hill & Norman partnership which became the Barry Island Slate & Slab Co., who operated it as a slab department.

The mill dating from the St Brides United Slate & Slab era of the 1860s, had 3 saws and 2 planers, with a claimed capacity of 30 tons per month. It was driven by an 10hp steam engine which also wound the chain incline which replaced horse-whim haulage. The St Brides Welsh Slate & Slab Co. continued to operate it but it is unlikely that the

United Welsh Slate Co. did much with it. In 1889 the landlord, J. Beynon Harries of Llanelli seized it, presumably in lieu of unpaid rent, repaired the machinery and re-appointed as manager Price Roberts a Caernarfonshire man who had worked here and Porthgain for 40 years.

Harries apparently found a stock of large slabs, probably a frustrated order, as he immediately advertised:

TRWYNLLWYD SLAB QUARRY TREVINE
FOR SALE, some excellent Slab Tables, measuring 8' x 3' and 1½" thick. Farmers and others requiring such articles will do well to inspect the stock at the above Quarry, the quality and workmanship of which are guaranteed equal to any in Wales.

By the middle of 1890 he had clearly got into production. Advertisements for the 'Renowned Trwynllwyd Slabs' averred to be 'Celebrated in All Markets', appeared regularly. Described as being 'Manufactured in Large Quantities' and in a 'Large Variety of Sizes'. These included 'Window Cills, Paving Stones, Grave Stones, Floorings, Slabs for Sanitary Work of all kinds, Head Stones, Mantelpieces, Kerb Stones, Gate Posts, Cuttings and Cisterns to order'.

It is unlikely that the venture lasted long and it had probably been idle for some years when it was offered for sale in 1898, and undoubtedly has not worked since.

It is remarkable that the quarter ton slabs advertised by Harries were somehow moved off site and that the boiler was kept fed with coal.

Remains Quarry area (now virtually inaccessible) is a working into almost the full height of the cliffs, with a sloping face conforming to the dip of the rock. At the clifftop are the walls of a nice little mill building with engine or boiler house alongside. In front of which the rock has been cut away to allow a straight haul for a chain or similar incline. These are possible remains of a sheave mounting. Quarry waste was dumped on the beach to be dispersed by the tides. The mill waste contains circular sawn ends.

Area 2 Central Pembrokeshire

Three of the region's larger quarries are in this area, Sealyham being the most significant. It was worked with varying degrees of success for at least three-quarters of a century although it was only a serious producer for about ten years during the 1860-70s boom.

Summerton, a bigger excavation although it produced less saleable product is technically interesting but tantalisingly difficult to interpret and has few records extant.

The third, Cronllwyn was potentially an excellent site, easy to work and close to Fishguard. Unfortunately it ran into geological difficulties after only a few years of working. It and Summerton, were among the first in the region to have slab-sawing machinery but produced curiously little slab.

Fishguard was the main port of shipment for the area. Although by the 19th century Haverfordwest's importance as a port had declined, its rail connection in the early 1850s made it a centre for the slate trade. In the late 1870s there were four slate merchants in the town including Ashton & Son of Goat Street who also dealt in enamelled slate. It is unlikely that Ashtons did their own enamelling, such items like much of the slate these merchants were selling at this time, would have come in by rail from other areas.

Both the two railways, the North Pembrokeshire and Fishguard Railway of 1895/9 and the G.W.R. Fishguard extension of 1906, opened too late to have any slate significance.

SM948336	Pantyphillip	
948374	Windy Hall	
960275	Sealyham	*
967341	Pant y Wrach	
971346	Esgyrn	*
985353	Cronllwyn	*

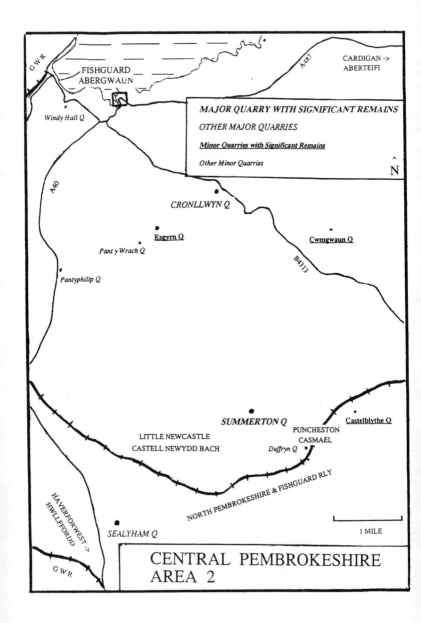

CARDIGAN -> ABERTEIFI

FISHGUARD
ABERGWAUN

GWR

A487

MAJOR QUARRY WITH SIGNIFICANT REMAINS

OTHER MAJOR QUARRIES

<u>*Minor Quarries with Significant Remains*</u>

Other Minor Quarries

^N

Windy Hall Q

A40

CRONLLWYN Q

Esgyrn Q

Cwmgwaun Q

Pant y Wrach Q

B4313

Pantyphilip Q

SUMMERTON Q

Castelblythe Q

LITTLE NEWCASTLE
CASTELL NEWYDD BACH

PUNCHESTON
CASMAEL

Duffryn Q

NORTH PEMBROKESHIRE & FISHGUARD RLY

HAVERFORWEST ->
HWLLFFORDD

SEALYHAM Q

1 MILE

GWR

CENTRAL PEMBROKESHIRE
AREA 2

992302   Summerton **
SN007292   Dyffryn
010344   Cwmgwaun *
017301   Castleblythe *

CASTLEBLYTHE (Gwarn) SN017301

Hillside quarry, possibly worked on and off for much of 19th century/early 20th century. In 1884 a lease was taken by Henry Ledgard and John Davies but it is not known if they worked it. The adjacent N.P. & F.Rly was not used.

Not to be confused with a quarry of the same name at SN020294 which appears to have yielded only rough building stone.

Remains Main working reached through a cutting in an earlier tip. Sole artifacts, some bar rail. Two trials are nearby. Used a pre-existing farm road.

CRONLLWYN SM985353

Hillside quarrying with gallery working, deepened into pits. Little is known of its origins but it may have been the Capel quarry which was leased for one year by three Fishguard slaters in 1789.

It was clearly already well developed when the lease was offered for sale in 1846. It was described as having carpenter's and blacksmith's shops, a powder magazine and a waterwheel with 'circular sawing machine plant'. Equipment included several hundred yards of tramway track, wagons, barrows, tools and implements. The lease at £50 p.a. was described as being 27 years unexpired which on a 40 or 50 year term would date its granting to 1833 or 1823. It was said to have produced £500 annual profit with wages and expenses of £26 per week, suggesting a yearly sale approaching 1000 tons.

It was bought by the Cronllwyn Slate Co. which had been formed the previous year. Quite what they did is uncertain. Nothing came of their plans to lay a railway to

Fishguard and within two years they were (unsuccessfully) trying to sell out, describing the quarry as being in 'Full Work'.

It seems to have been idle when it was bought by John Davies who floated the Pembrokeshire Slate Co. in 1864. Directors were, William Page, Mayor of Nottingham, William Parsons, Ex-mayor of Nottingham, Thomas Dickson and Stephen Dickson both also of Nottingham and, of course, John Davies who sold them the lease for £4000 cash plus £6000 in shares. The rent was £40 p.a. merging to 1/16th, the directors agreeing to waive their fees until a 15% dividend could be paid. The Prospectus published in 1865 said that there were '3 galleries, an inclined plane and ample water', no mention being made of buildings or machinery. Since it said that it needed 'only clearing the levels and laying rails' to reopen, indicating that the rails had been sold, suggests that the saws etc. may have also gone.

William Pritchard who had been in charge at Porthgain was brought in as manager. It had been stated that the property covered two veins, only one of which had been worked, (and presumably worked out). Pritchard soon discovered that Granite posts effectively prevented the second vein being worked and in 1866 he sought to extend the holding to try to reach it. In 1866 the problems were recognised as insuperable and the company was wound up in 1868.

Whilst it is unlikely that there was any working after that, there was a promise of prosperity in the early 1870s when the Rosebush, Fishguard and Goedic Railway was proposed as an extension of the then unbuilt Maenclochog Railway. The line was planned to run through the lower workings of Cronllwyn Quarry which, it was claimed, could then be reopened 'to the great profit of all concerned'. This of course, never happened.

Remains No buildings survive, the drainage/access tunnel which passed under the farm road from the largest of the workings has long since collapsed, but there is some trace of the galleries. There is a smaller working face to the north which may also have had an access tunnel.

Next to the public house at Llanychaer there was a smithy which is said to have provided a tool sharpening facility for the quarrymen. Perhaps indicating that the later lessees did not use the blacksmith's shop.

CWMGWAUN SN010344

There were several places in the valley where a shaley rock was dug, e.g. Garn 998351, Trellwyn 011352 and Pen yr Allt Ddu 042342, but this is the only one to have apparently yielded a merchantable slate. Nothing known but may have been active around 1870.

Remains Tiny scratchings in forestry. Two tunnels (25yd & 10yd) suggest an attempt to roof up for underground working. The access track is now a footpath.

DYFFRYN SN007292

A shallow hillside working leased by the Rev. Charles Barham to David and Benjamin Rees in 1867 for £20 p.a. merging to a royalty of 1/18th. Apparently already abandoned by 1895 when the closely adjacent N.P. & F. Rly opened.

Remains Long and much overgrown face. Formation of a railed tipping run. Roofing slate trimming waste.

ESGYRN SM971346 & 975347

Two entirely separate hillside quarries in common ownership which may have worked for some time before J.F.N. Hewett obtained a 40 year lease in 1866, and registered the Esgyrn Slate Quarry Co. with a capital of £15,000. The advertisement seeking investors showed directors as J.F.N. Hewett (managing) and C. Allen, both from Haverfordwest, with A. Goolde of Gloucester and George Homfray late of Tredegar (An Ironmaster?). The royalty was vaguely defined as 'liberal' and the profits to prospective investors were anticipated to be '70%-90% p.a.'.

It is not known how much money was actually raised, or apart from the driving of an abortive tunnel, how much work was done before Hewett died (aged 33) of a drug overdose described as 'Inadvertent'.

The lease was obtained by Thomas Carter, a Swansea colliery owner who formed the Eskern Slate & Slab Quarries Co. in 1873. The company was to buy the lease from him for £22,500 in shares as well as a substantial but obscure sum in cash. Apparently with the slate market booming Carter's London associates, Clark & Holden were able to raise some £35,000. Each being given £250 in shares for their trouble. There seems to have been no quarrying done and in 1876 the company was subject to a High Court winding up order, which was accompanied by severe censure from the judge.

Remains The easterly site is just a quarry face. The westerly is a cutting with some signs of production. Below it is the 150yd exploratory tunnel, inside which are some sleepers and fragments of bridge rail.

PANTYPHILLIP SM948336

A modest operation which appears to have worked, probably intermittently, at least from c1830 to near the end of the 19th century producing mainly slab and block. It has in late years been used for bulk stone and perhaps some slab.

Remains Quarried area only.

PANT Y WRACH SM967341

Nothing known until the farm was advertised for sale in 1871 and also in 1875 as including a slate quarry. It was offered again in 1887 as a 'Slate quarry within easy reach of the projected Letterston station' (Not opened until 1895!). Very little extraction was done, all of it probably before the above mentions.

Remains Shallow excavation. Adit at 968342 is almost certainly a metal trial, but it is just possible it was a slate investigation.

SEALYHAM SM960275

Originally a small hillside working used by the Taylors of Sealyham as a source of slate for estate use. William Tucker Edwardes, whose father had married into the family, seems to have commenced commercial exploitation when he inherited in 1825.

When Watkin Scale bought the lease in 1847, work had already been forced to go downward since a driveway limited the advance of the face. The resultant pit was dewatered by a water wheel pump fed from an old mill leat.

It is clear that Scale had great confidence in his acquisition as he engaged William Pritchard an experienced north Wales quarryman, and within three weeks of taking possession was advertising:

SEALYHAM QUARRY

The Public are respectfully informed that the above named quarry is now being reopened on a large scale for the purpose of raising an unlimited quantity of the BEST BLUE SLATES. The quality of the slates is well known in the County of Pembroke to be equal in colour and superior in strength to the best north Wales, while it far surpasses in both respects any slate that has yet been discovered in south Wales. As the operations of reopening will prevent any great quantity of slates from being raised in the next 2 months, those parties who may require an immediate supply are respectfully requested to make their wants known to the Proprietor, W.E. Wakin Scale, Copper Mine St Davids or to William Pritchard, Sealyham Quarry Haverfordwest.

N.B. The quarry is 8m from Haverfordwest on the Fishguard Road.

It is said that Scale persuaded William Edwardes to divert his driveway and build a new bridge so that the quarrying face could advance. However the so-called new driveway was already in existence and the bridge work was a rebuild, so in fact Edwardes merely agreed to the stopping up of a redundant route.

Lack of trade having forced Scale to give up in 1851, Edwardes advertised for new tenants stating that, 'It is situate about half a mile from the South Wales Railroad'. Clearly he was referring to the proposed Fishguard line, construction of which was suspended later that year and only resumed by the GWR over fifty years later. This advertisement said that, 'Water machinery is used', and it also referred to the site as a 'Slate and Slab Quarry'. Whilst it is tempting to conclude that powered sawing was being done, all evidence suggests that the 'water machinery' was the pump.

No let was made until 1855 when it was taken by brothers Thomas & John Rees of Broadmoor Farm, Wolfscastle. They advertised at intervals in the local press, e.g. in 1859:

To Builders, Masons &c.
Sealyham Metallic Slate Quarry
Warranted to be as good in quality as any Slates in Wales. Situate 7m from Haverfordwest within a quarter of a mile of the turnpike road leading from Haverfordwest to Fishguard. Good easy road to come out to the turnpike.

Good Locals		per 1000	15/- (75p)
Princesses	24 x 14	per 1260	£8. 0. 0
Duchesses	24 x 12		£7. 0. 0
"	22 x 11		£6. 0. 0
Countesses	20 x 10		£4.15. 0 (£4.75)
"	18 x 10		£3.15. 0 (£3.75)
"	18 x 9		£3. 0. 0

Lords	16 x 10	£3. 0. 0
Ladies	16 x 8	£2. 5. 0 (£2.25)
"	14 x 8	£1. 10. 0 (£1.50)

Apply to Mr John Rees Broadmoor Wolfscastle

The naming of sizes approximately conformed to those of North Wales, (except that 16 x 10 were known there as Wide Ladies). Prices of the largest sizes were a little below the First Quality offerings from their main competitor, Porthgain but all others were dearer.

In 1860 the 'Nobility names' were dropped and the list widened to include 22 x 11 & 20 x 12. In spite of the general hardening of the market, Porthgain did not raise their prices, neither did Sealyham on their smallest sizes. Presumably in order to make their list look cheap they slashed 10/- (50p) off the largest, for which there was little demand. However the intermediate sizes which was where most of their trade lay, they raised by up to 10/- (50p). They also put Locals up to 16/- (80p), well above Porthgain as well as introducing a new category, 'Best Dry Tiling' at £1 per 1000, which were probably Locals under another name. They also slipped in an insidious little hike in their 'sizes' rates by selling in 1250 instead of 1260.

Taking into account the high carriage costs, Sealyham slates must have been the dearest in Pembrokeshire and this undoubtedly contributed to Thomas Rees' bankruptcy in June 1862 and the collapse of the partnership.

The quarry was described as being idle in 1866 when a new lease was granted to Hugh Davies at a rent of £100 p.a. plus 1/40th ad valorem of sales. He was joined in 1869 by Elias and Samuel Hughes from Caernarfonshire. Their workforce was not large as the 1871 census showed only 10 men in the parish as slate workers, 4 besides the Hughes' being from Caernarfonshire and 3 from Llanrian (ex. Porthgain men?).

The Hughes' dropped out in 1876 and Thomas Williams, manager at Porthgain, unhappy at the way things were going there and spurred by the North Wales producers having yet again substantially raised their prices (by 15% on Seconds), seized the opportunity to take on their holding. The energetic Williams set about clearing the pit of debris, but within months water broke in, flooding the pit.

Since 1858 when William Edwardes died, lessees had found his widow Anna distinctly difficult and Davies' installation of an 8 hp steam engine to uphaul from the pit cannot have pleased her. An offer to pay a rent of £300 p.a. failed to persuade her to allow 'encroachment on the plantations' which would have 'affected the view from the carriage drive'. It may well have been her opposition to quarry improvements which contributed to the inundation.

Anna Edwardes died in 1877 and her son J.O. Tucker Edwardes, (the formidable 'Captain Jack', original breeder of the Sealyham dogs), obtained a private report from his Land Agent, T. Rule Owen, as to the quarries potential. Owen said that money needed to be spent on diverting the river, extending the quarry and possibly going underground, he also said that 'Fifty per cent is paid for Sealyham slates over those raised in the county' (which was of course quite untrue).

Edwardes granted a fresh 40 year lease which was slightly more favourable as the £100 rent merged into the royalty instead of being in addition to it. Thus encouraged Davies & Williams could then set about sorting out the mess. Styling themselves first Davies & Co., then The Sealyham Slate Company and raising money on mortgage, they cut a deep channel 540' long to divert the river Anghof and put in a new water powered pumping system. They were soon claiming to have 8 slatemakers at work making slates to the value of £120 to £160 per week on which they said they were making 50% profit, which right on the crest of the boom may well have been correct.

They installed a second steam engine, a 12 hp Robey and proposed to 'develop slab manufacture using water power at a 20ft head'.

Williams, very much the dominant partner, had ambitious ideas. He said he intended to employ 80 slatemakers, 30 quarrymen and 25 labourers at an average weekly wage respectively of 25/- (£1.25), 23/- (£1.15) and 18/- (90p). Good money indeed but even with two engine drivers, a smith and striker as well as a manager and a clerk, their outgoings would be under £10,000 p.a. which according to Williams would yield £30,720 in slates plus the value of any slab. He proposed to work on 3 galleries as a preliminary to going underground. He planned to spend over £7000 on another waterwheel and machinery and on cottages at Wolfscastle to house the increased workforce. Little if any of these plans were carried out.

An advertisement appeared in January 1879:

> Sealyham Slate & Slab Co. are now making at the quarry. Locals and Sizes of superior quality. No small Sized slates made. The Locals are far superior in quality and size to any made before, so much so as to be quite good enough for any dry roofing (i.e. laid without torching with mortar). All communications sent to the Secretary will receive prompt attention. Terms cash for small amounts. T. Williams, Manager.

By the Summer of 1879 the old title had been resumed and it was obvious from their advertising that they realised that demand and prices were dropping fast:

> The Sealyham Slate Company beg to inform the public that their quarry is now fully developed. In view of the large increase in slatemaking they have decided on a considerable reduction in the prices of slates, both Locals & Sizes. All communications addressed to the Secretary will be promptly attended to – Thos. Williams, Manager.

Falling prices and a shrinking market failed to dim Williams' optimism. At a public meeting in support of the proposed Rosebush & Fishguard Railway (eventually the North Pembroke & Fishguard Railway), he said that the railway would reduce his carriage costs to Fishguard from 6/- (30p) per ton to 1/- (5p), thus he would be contributing £4000 p.a. to the railway's revenues. Admittedly he was already sending a few tons to Wexford via Fishguard, but a prediction of 80,000 tons (which would have called for over 2000 men) stretched credulity somewhat.

Williams left in 1881 but despite the depressed state of trade which hastened his departure, Sealyham Slate was formally registered as a company in 1883. Backed by A.S. Hammond, J.G. Powers, T. Lewis, W. Vaughan and H.D. Harries, all local men, plus D.J. Meyler a Swansea draper and G.W. Meyler of Hendon (a relative?) with Daniel Lewis as manager. Although Hugh Davies initiated the flotation he took no part in it. By 1885 having done little or no business, 115,000 slates held at Fishguard were auctioned and pressed by mortgagees, the quarry plant was sold. Particulars included the two engines plus engine houses, both described as for haulage, also a 14' water wheel (the pumping wheel?). Two Saw Tables with gearing and a Planing Machine also with gearing were listed. Interestingly the seven dressing sheds were described as 'Portable'.

E. Harries bought the plant and was granted a new lease at £100 p.a. (merging to a royalty) in 1887 but whether he worked is unclear. He did not advertise until 1890 when his announcements were redolent of stock being sold off:

SEALYHAM QUARRY
Local Slates – Slabs & Stone are now on sale at the above quarry.

Later that year T. Rule Owen, seemingly backed by H. Birch of Porthgain quarry, floated the New Sealyham Slate Co. Other directors were three London men, Henry King an engineer, F. Fenton a broker, R.B. Heinkley a merchant and Joseph Hetherington described as a quarry manager of Porthgain (probably Birch's nominee). T.H. Owen (T.R. Owen's son?) was company secretary. Daniel Lewis was re-engaged as manager.

It seems to have been a genuine attempt to run the quarry as the £5000 capital was modest and no one stood to make a killing on the transfer of the lease. Harries was paid £500 cash plus £400 in shares with a further £1500 in profit-related instalments, not too excessive considering it included all machinery and stock.

The appeal for subscriptions stated that:

'The quarries on which a large amount of capital has been laid out are in good working order and capable of extended production. The slate has a wide reputation for exceptional durability and toughness being only surpassed by the first quality of the Caernarvonshire slate, the second quality of which being heavier than the Sealyham slate and therefore more costly to work and to handle. The machinery and plant have just been put into thorough repair.'

The customary report made no pretence of independence, being a rehash of Owen's report of 1877. He described himself as 'A well-known Surveyor of long experience who has for many years exceptional means of knowledge both of the quarries and of the locality.'

Owen stated that:

'I have known these quarries for 35 years and as a general remark may say that for quality of material no Blue Slate quarry in South Wales can approach them and that they have been successfully worked on a small scale for many years. I consider that a large proportion of the best slate remains to be worked and it will be easy to run as the bed has escaped the contortion which so frequently renders veins and other mineral properties in Pembrokeshire less valuable and difficult to work. As to the durability of the slate, the best proof you can have is the fact that little other slate has been used in the country with the exception of Caernarvonshire Slates, and that houses roofed with it 80 and 100 years ago are still sound. It is besides a clean warm coloured slate free from discoloration but as this slate bed where worked has a very deep heading over it, the mode of working should be altered. I consider the best method of doing this would be by underground workings or galleries. By this system much expense would be saved and a still better quality of slate more quickly obtained. I have no hesitation in saying that the quarry if worked on a moderate scale and in a systematic way would prove a good investment for capital.'

Potential investors were also told that 30,000 sized slates and 50,000 Locals were already being made each month at an alleged annual net profit of £1000, with of course, the usual assurance that this output could be much larger. They were not told that all work was into the overhang (1), or that the poor split often resulted in slates being warped.

Fishguard was mentioned as a port but Haverfordwest only as railhead, emphasising the decline of its shipping by this time. Interestingly much was made of the harbour improvements at Solva which were, 'providing facilities for easy and rapid shipment, for the remarkably active development of trade in south Wales is opening up new markets which the company will take full advantage of.' Solva was 4 miles further than Haverfordwest, involving up to 10/- (50p) extra carriage on a thousand slates, indicating that coastwise freights remained much cheaper than rail charges.

(1) Where due to topography, quarrying has to advance in the direction of the Dip, a dangerous and difficult overhang results. This can be ameliorated by Gallery working or avoided by Underground working – hence the earlier plans that these methods be used here.

This venture failed after less than three years, apparently without making any product and scarcely months before the opening of the N.P. & F. Rly might have facilitated transport.

Both 'Captain Jack' and his son (also John) having died in 1891, the estate passed through the hands of several relatives. The quarry was briefly held but not worked in the late 1890s by the shadowy California & Mexico Mining Co. Some very restricted working may have been done during the slate shortage around 1903.

Remains Some 300 yards from Sealyham house, now the Sealyham Activity Centre, the carriage drive turns down to the left to follow its 'new' route across Quarry Bridge to Wolfscastle village. The 'old' route is traceable through the trees passing on the left old, overgrown buildings, spoken of as cottages but may be remnants of an old mill and the putative site of the water wheel of the original pump. The line of the leat is now lost by afforestation.

Nearing the flooded quarry is a shaft and a possible run-in adit intersecting it, (an attempt at underground working?). A trench seems to have accommodated the flat-rods for the early pump and it is just possible to confirm map evidence that its spillway was extended to discharge into the diverted river, suggesting that it remained in use for a time after the 1877 pump was installed.

The original course of the river is obvious, immediately in front of the quarry pit.

The wheelpit for the later pump and its spillway discharging into the deep gash of the diverted river, is in a cutting a little way beyond at the end of the embankment which carried water to drive the wheel. Opposite, the pump pipe rises from the water.

To the south-west matters become more enigmatic. There are two distinct waste run levels, both of which block the 'old' line of the river. The lower level, overlain by the upper, was the mapped site of one 'Engine House', the other being on the more extensive upper level. It has not been possible to positively identify the position of either. It is just feasible, amongst the copious vegetation to locate the incline which the upper engine would have wound. If the lower engine also wound, any associated incline has been buried under what appears to be a later tipping run. There is no indication that two enginemen were ever employed so one must assume that use of the lower, earlier engine was abandoned when or shortly after, the upper, later engine was installed.

No evidence of any kind has been found of a building for the saws and planer, which presumably were on the upper level and powered by the winding engine, it being of as much as 12hp supports this, neither is there evidence of water-power having been used for sawing. At the same time no sawn ends, even hand sawn ones have been found and the 1890 advertisements are the only known occasions that slabs were actually offered for sale. One must conclude that slab output was minimal.

Beyond the quarry, the line of the 'old' carriage drive continues to Bryn Gomer.

SUMMERTON SM992302

A sizeable but frustratingly recondite site, believed to have been developed in the mid 1830s by the landlord the Rev. Thomas Martin. He is said to have spent a great deal of money on it but by the early 1840s, there were probably less than half a dozen men employed.

When was offered for sale in 1852, interestingly the Sale Particulars described it as a mine. Following the inevitably fulsome description of the product – 'Impartial judges say it surpasses the best north Wales slate' it went on to say,

'The machinery is the invention of the proprietor for the

manufacture and cutting of slate to an accuracy perfectly unobtainable by any other means and also as regards the largest classes with a saving of 200%.'

Regrettably the machinery is not described, but it would seem that slab was being cut by machinery other than sandsaws or any of the several sorts of circular saw by then in use.

The outcome of the sale is not known but in 1859 this advertisement appeared in the Haverfordwest and Milford Haven Telegraph:

> The Proprietor of these very extensive slate formations assures the public that he is now ready to receive orders for the several classes of slate annexed which are similar to those of the North Wales quarries.
>
> Duchesses 24 x 12 £8. 6. 0 (£8.30) per 1000
> Countesses 20 x 10 £5. 7. 0 (£5.35) per 1000
>
> Every other class to order. Locals at quarry £1.0.0 per 1000 or £1.5.0 (£1.25) at Haverfordwest.
>
> As the Proprietor is aware that assertions are valueless unless confirmed by positive facts, he desires it to be publicly known that he will make a reduction of 10% provided the produce of any slate mine through the whole of North Wales be found to be superior both in quality and manufacture to Sommerton (Sic) Slate.

The similarity of style suggests that it had not been sold in 1852 and one must assume that the 'Proprietor', encouraged by the firming of the market, had reopened after a period of idleness. Again the term 'mine' is used.

The prices suggest confidence in the product since Porthgain was offering 1260 of the same sized slates at £7.5.0 (£7.25) and £4.14.0 (£4.70) respectively and Locals at 14/- (70p) & 15/6 (77.5p). However offering just two stock sizes does not suggest a brisk trade.

Whilst there might be an assumption that through the

1850s the site was being worked by or on behalf of the Rev. Martin, when referring to a serious fall of rock in 1862, he said that it had caused his tenant's failure.

Later that year he attempted to sell the whole estate, although somewhat exaggerated claims were made of the excellence of the slate, the property seems to have been chiefly valued as farmland, it being stated that 'The surface soil is recumbent upon a slate stratum, which through its warm properties is conducive to quick vegetation', suggesting that the quarry was idle.

The estate unsold, the quarry was re-let in 1863, described as having been, 'Worked to a depth of 60 ft'. The new occupiers advertised in the Pembrokeshire Herald –

Messrs Earle & Cox beg to inform the gentry and farmers in the neighbourhood that they now have a large stock of Locals on hand at 15/- to 20/- per thousand at the quarry.

This could suggest that they were only making poor product, but it is possible that in this time of increasing demand they had a ready sale for the better slates and were trying to unload the duff stuff locally.

The estate was again offered for sale in 1865. Particulars mentioned ponds 88 chains to the north of the quarry area with a canal leading to the 'works'. This may suggest that by this time a fresh water source was in use probably associated with a second mill which certainly had one or more circular saws.

Little more is known except that the quarried area expanded during the 1870s, with closure apparently occurring during the bad times of the 1880s. Had the N.P. & F. Rly been available to it during the '60s/70s boom, its history might have been very different.

Remains The hillside working, deepened into a pit with a cutting for access and drainage is conventional enough, but almost everything else is highly enigmatic.

In the face are three adits, one of which has some

attempt at chambering. There used to be an air shaft some 300m northwest which suggests that tunnelling was extensive, but this is from earlier metal mining. Near the entrance to the cutting is a quantity of dressing waste, but no traces of sheds.

On the western rim are two substantial pillars, the one nearer the pit being wider at the top than the base, in front of it are two cantilevered platforms, which could be the landing of a vertical lift. The other pillar, and its counterpart on the opposite side could possibly be ropeway anchorages. Adjacent to the western pillars are the remains of two further pillars the purpose of which is not apparent.

A prominent feature is the 250m long embankment which might have been intended for a tramway and which maps show as having a 'canal' on its upper side fed from a watercourse leading in from a pond a mile to the east. This clearly led to the pit of a breast-shot wheel at the end of the embankment. Adjacent to the wheelpit is a curious structure with two arched voids beneath it, presumably the site of the 1830s 'cutting machinery'.

The waterway appears to have been blocked by tipping (but may have been culverted). Maps suggest that it was replaced, or supplemented by a leat running behind the quarry, the embankment then forming a dam to supply the later mill, overgrown vestiges of which with its wheelpit, are in front of the arched structure. Although there are a number of circular-sawn ends at the later mill site, no such ends have been found adjacent to the 'arches', but ends with diagonal cuts are there. This could indicate the use of toothed handsaws, but the regularity of the cuts tempts one to speculate that they were made by a reciprocating powered saw of unusual type.

WINDY HALL SM948374

Predominately rough block but apparently did produce some roofing material.
Remains Quarry face.

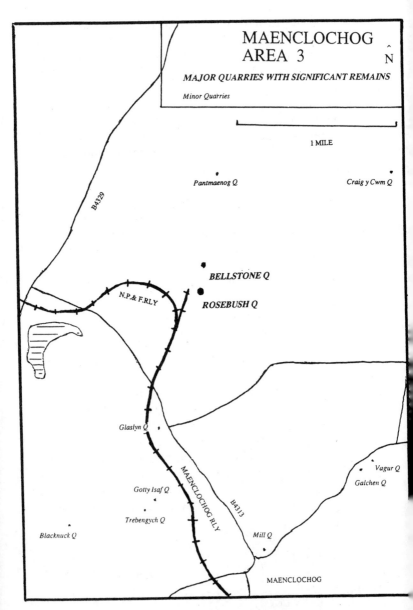

MAENCLOCHOG
AREA 3

MAJOR QUARRIES WITH SIGNIFICANT REMAINS

Minor Quarries

1 MILE

Pantmaenog Q

Craig y Cwm Q

B4329

BELLSTONE Q

N.P.& F.RLY

ROSEBUSH Q

Glaslyn Q

MAENCLOCHOG RLY

B4313

Vagur Q

Galchen Q

Gotty Isaf Q

Trebengych Q

Blacknuck Q

Mill Q

MAENCLOCHOG

Area 3 Maenclochog

Near the village of Maenclochog on the southern flank of the Preseli Hills, are several exposures of excellent slate. They were most notably worked at Bellstone and Rosebush, Bellstone ranking briefly around 1830 as one of the largest in the region.

Rosebush, following its development by a farsighted and long pocketed owner, was for a few years in the 1870s the leading slate working of south west Wales creating a substantial community which still survives. Apart from Minllyn in the upper Dyfi valley, it was the only Welsh slate quarry to have a standard gauge railway branch built to serve it. Unfortunately the late 1870s collapse of the market made it one of the great might-have-beens of the Welsh slate industry.

SN063278	Blacknuck		
073281	Trebengych		
073282	Gotty Isaf		
076286	Glaslyn		
079300	Rosebush	***	(R)
079303	Bellstone	*	
080313	Pantmaenog		
085275	Mill		
095283	Galchen		
096284	Vagur		
097312	Craig y Cwm		

BELLSTONE (Precelly) SN079303

Following his lack of success at Craig y Cwm, J.F. Barham moved here at the end of 1825. The quarry had clearly been operating long before this as several churches and mansions were roofed with Bellstone slate in the 18th century.

For a short time Barham seems to have re-employed all 60 of his Craig y Cwm men but, presumably because of the less arduous conditions, on lower wages. Slate Makers were at first on 1/8 (8.3p) per day, but later appear to have been on some kind of piece work at 6/- (30p) per 1250 slates made. There is record of a Slate Maker earning 13/6 (67.5p) in a week by making 2260 slates. Quarrymen got 1/3 (6.25p), labourers 1/- (5p) and boys 6d to 9d (2.5p - 3.75p). A carpenter and mason were employed at 1/8 (8.3p) per day and four miners at 2/- (10p). If these miners were employed to cut a tunnel, then work must have been well established by the time Barham took over.

Within a year his payroll had fallen to ten and by 1834 it was being worked by John & Lewis Lawrence apparently as sub-tenants of Barham, who surrendered the lease the following year.

The land having passed from Sir John Owen to his son Hugh Owen Owen, the latter let it to a curious syndicate of Haverfordwest men comprising 2 Upholsterers, 2 Merchants, a Druggist, an Ironmonger and a 'Gent'. Having spent a great deal of money with little prospect of a return and finding the cartage cost of 7/- (35p) made their product uncompetitive they, in conjunction with their landlord made an informal arrangement in 1837 for it to be worked by T.R. Hutton of London. Hutton paid a little over £300 ingoings to the syndicate for stock on hand etc. and was required to pay £1000 each to Owen and to the syndicate after 12 months. He undertook to collect the syndicate's outstanding debts of almost £1900.

There appears to have been no rent, just a 1/12th royalty. Some of the terms were unexceptionable, such as that a weighing machine be installed, that proper records be available for inspection, that working was to be continuous save for snow and for a 14 day harvest period and that all rubbish had to be tipped on the west side of the road. However the requirement that 50 men must be immediately employed, increasing to 100 after six months and 200 after three years was quite impossibly onerous. It is obvious that the employment requirements were not met as the 1841 census shows only 10 men in the parish as quarrymen.

A wide variety of slates were offered, as surviving 1845 hand-written lists show.

1st Duchesses	24 x 12	3 tons per mil	£5.10.0 (£5.50)
2nd "	22 x 11	2½ "	£4. 0.0
1st Countesses	20 x 10	2 "	£3. 5.0 (£3.25)
2nd "	18 x 9	1½ "	£2. 0.0
1st Ladies	16 x 8	1¼ "	£1. 8.0 (£1.40)
2nd Ladies	14 x 7	1 "	£0.15.0 (75p)
Doubles	13 x 6½	15 cwt "	£0.10.0 (50p)
Locals		16 " 1000	£0.15.0 (75p)
Water marked Locals		" "	£0.13.0 (65p)

One list has carriage charges 'To wharf' pencilled in.

1st Duchesses	21/-	(£1.05)	per mil of 1260
2nd "	17/6	(87.5p)	"
1st Countesses	15/-	(75p)	"
2nd "	10/6	(52.5p)	"
1st Ladies	9/-	(45p)	"
2nd Ladies	7/-	(35p)	"
Doubles	6/-	(30p)	"
Locals	do		per ten hundred (sic)

The thickness of the Tally (sized) slates works out at .170", only slightly more than north Wales Bests, but priced at over a third less.

The terms '1st' and '2nd' are unusual, 22 x 11 were normally known as Narrow Duchesses, 18 x 9 as Viscountesses, 14 x 7 as Narrow Ladies. The Doubles were an odd size, 12 x 6 being the recognised dimensions.

To confound this sizing further the introduction of a further five was proposed –

Wide Duchesses	24 x 14	3½t per mil.	(N. Wales Princesses)
Wide Countesses	20 x 12	2¼ "	(" Broad Countesses)
Short Countesses	18 x 10	1¾ "	(" Small Countesses)
Wide Ladies	16 x 10	1½ "	(Same as N. Wales)
Small Ladies	14 x 8	1 "	(" ")

In fact almost no slates larger than 1st Ladies were sold and most of these went out in small quantities sometimes at no more than 16/- (80p) per mil. The late 1844 purchase by the Commissioners of the Gas Works, Haverfordwest of 2½ mil of these, charged at £3.2.6 (£3.12) including carriage being a relatively large order.

Only one substantial order has been identified. In 1841 Belgian merchants, Le Brasseur bought 20 mil of 1st Ladies and 40 mil of 2nd Ladies. Prices ex-quarry were £1.0.0 and 14/- (70p) per mil respectively. Carriage and Freight for this 45 ton load to Ostend totalled over £25, more than half of which was carriage to Fishguard.

Overwhelmingly sales were of Locals, at prices from 14/- (70p) down to 10/- (50p) per 1000. In 1845 the last year of production, 550 1st Duchesses and 5670 1st Ladies were made but none were sold, 1850 1st Countesses were made, only 450 being sold. No 2nd Countesses were made but 300 were sold from stock. Their biggest order (£3.00!) was for 4000 2nd Ladies which was met from stock. They made 237,500 Locals, selling 137,000 of them.

When production ceased the inventory showed a stock of 721,400 of which 531,250 were Locals. This inventory also listed a pathetically small total of equipment; An office table and eight chairs, a smithy with vice, 'grinding stone', anvil and bellows. A carpenter's bench and stool, two trams 'much out of repair', valued at 15/- (75p) also a 'sawing machine with flywheel' (i.e. a hand-powered circular saw). These were all sold then or shortly afterwards.

Sales continued from stock, at much reduced prices (e.g. 2nd Countesses @ 20/- (£1), 2nd Ladies @ 10/- (50p). Again sales were mostly of Locals, at prices as low as 5/- (25p) or even 2/6 (12.5p) per 1000, most invoices being for less than £1, some a mere 1/- (5p).

Selling slates was one thing, getting paid for them another. Some customers took up to a year to pay off accounts which even by the standards of the time were trifling. In 1850, the last year of trading, sales were well under £100 and debtors totalled over £154, of which almost £110 was classed as Bad Debt (including the £73.6.6 for goods and carriage of the 1841 Belgian order!)

In 1853 what remained of the equipment; 30 lengths of bar rail, 8 turnouts and 22 cast-iron wheels and the remaining stock of 515,000 slates, almost all Locals, were auctioned off.

In 1858 there was a brief announcement in the local press that 'Precelly quarry was at work' shortly followed by another naming Robert Jones as manager. The operator, one assumes, was John Davies, since Sir Hugh Owen, as he now was, released land to him for tipping in 1862. In 1866 John Davies with his friend Ledgard, formed the Bellstone Slate Co. (This being the first use of that name, previously having been known as Precelly.) There seems to be little evidence that much work was done even in this boom era, although in 1866 further land was granted for tipping.

When Cropper became involved at Rosebush in 1869 the quarry was idle but Sir Hugh Owen must have had hopes of a let as he insisted that the possible needs of Bellstone for water etc. be safeguarded.

In 1881 undeterred by the poor state of trade but encouraged by the availability of the Maenclochog Railway, the Bellstone Slate Quarries Co. was formed to take on the higgledy-piggledy remains of the earlier operators. Capital was £30,000 and subscribers, all London men were, D.A. Rees, J.E.B. White, J. Stowell, J.S. Fairfax G. Lund, S. Birch, W.G. Hanning. Sir Hugh Owen, was persuaded to take 30 of the £100 shares.

An unnamed visitor was prevailed upon to comment, possibly after being lunched rather well at the Precelly Hotel,

'This is essentially a slate quarry with the most beautiful cleavage I have ever seen. Now that it has been resuscitated and an influential company formed with a first class body of directors, it may be expected to turn out a treasure It faces the right way, has unlimited tip room, the same water that supplies its neighbour Rosebush, Mr Cropper's quarry, and is within a few yards of the Maenclochog Railway.'

They advertised in the local press during the Summer of 1882:

'SLATES! SLATES!
70,000 Local slates for cottages, outhouses &c are now on sale at Bellstone Quarries, Rosebush. Apply to Mr Phillips, Manager.

Repeated advertisements showing an undiminished stock suggests that sales were not brisk. The closure of the railway later that year, effectively ended any hope of survival. Final winding up came in 1889 ironically just prior to the recovery of slate prices.

Remains Although the workings were divided into 4 districts, North, Middle, New and Bayley's, it appears today as three workings which in seemingly unplanned fashion were deepened into pits, accessed and drainage by cuttings. The largest, southernmost pit also had a tunnel. In spite of great vertical distances the only incline was from the tunnel down to a rubbish area, extensive use being made of steep cart roads. There are a number of dressing sheds including a lean-to in an access cutting.

At ground level the manager's house is still in occupation and on the tips immediately in front of it are domestic outbuildings which may have been stabling. There is a vast tonnage of spoil. There are small trials in the forestry to the north east.

BLACKNUCK SN063278
Hillside quarry probably briefly worked in the 1870s when it was held on a lease at a rent of £20 p.a., up to £10 of which was deductible against a royalty of 1/16th ad valorem. A

lease was still in force when the freehold was sold in 1889 but it is not known if it was then being worked.
Remains Face, heavily overgrown.

CRAIG Y CWM SN097312

In 1825 on land owned by Rev. Charles Barham, J.F. Barham (his son?) set some 60 men the task of building an access track and digging slate at this inhospitable (1500' asl) location. Apparently he employed a foreman Thomas Sterling @ £5 per month of 4 weeks; 12 Slaters @ 2/3 (11p) per day, 6 Quarrymen @ 1/8 (8.3p) 40 Labourers @ 1/4 (6.7p) and 3 Boys at 6d-9d (2.5-3.75p). Clearly, as was widespread in the region, no Bargain system was operated and the men who made the slates were separate from those who won the rock. The fact that the quarry was being opened up accounts for the high proportion of Labourers to skilled men.

After 4 months work was abandoned, almost all the men being relocated at Bellstone. Some work seems to have been done later as there is record of slate destined for Belgium being carried from here in 1841, suggesting the possibility that it was then being worked by Hutton of Bellstone.
Remains Two excavations and access track, possible traces of a small building.

GALCHEN SN095283

A lease was granted in 1911 to dig for slate on Galchen (Fawr) Farm. Clearly unsuccessful.
Remains Slight traces of excavation. Access track.

GLASLYN SN076286

Putative site.
Remains Possible excavation.

GOTTY ISAF SN073282

Tiny hillside quarry possibly yielded only rough block.
Remains Excavation only.

MILL QUARRY SN085275

A small, shallow pit working. No record has been found and it appears to have been abandoned at an early date. The enumerator of the 1851 census remarked that there being only four quarrymen in the village of Maenclochog was due to the quarry there having recently closed. It is not known if this was the quarry he was referring to or if it was say, Bellstone.

This may have been the quarry which Essex Rees leased at the end of the century but did not work.

Remains Overgrown pit and tips covered with several inches of solid earth. Nearby walling is made of rough slab but trimming waste confirms the making of roofing slate. There is a building with a fireplace and an obvious access track. Traces of slate debris suggest that some tipping and possibly excavation was done on the far side of the road.

ROSEBUSH SN079300

The only undertaking in the region to operate on a really large scale (albeit briefly) and certainly the only one to have its own railway.

The early history is obscure, it does seem that T.R. Hutton also took rights to this land when he commenced at Bellstone in 1837. It is not known if he worked here or even if any quarrying had been done at this time, but it is unlikely that such obvious outcrops could have been ignored. In 1842 the land was bought by William Young but again we do not know what work if any was done and in 1862 he sold on to William Williams, a Narberth Draper. Williams must have died soon afterwards as in 1863 his widow, Mary, let it to John Davies and William Keylock.

In October the following year this item appeared in the *Mining Journal:*

'There are several rather valuable veins of slate in the northern district of Pembrokeshire and some 20 or 30 years ago the extensive quarries on the breast of the

Precelly mountains near Maenclochog were worked and an enormous capital sunk there. These quarries either from want of capital, bad management or some other cause have ceased working for a number of years until a short time ago they were started by a London company and a good many hands are now employed. The same company have taken or are in treaty for commencing to work other quarries in the same county including Llangolman, Llandilo, Tyrch &c. The extraordinary demand for slates has, no doubt, been the chief inducement in taking these quarries and it is to be hoped that they will turn out profitable to the enterprising speculators.'

This report like so many in the Mining Journal at the time would have been submitted by the promoters and the style of this one is redolent of John Davies himself and refers to the Rosebush Slate Co. which he and Keylock set up, obtaining capital from amongst others, a Mr Hodges. Serious work must have been intended as some trouble was taken to obtain a reduction in royalty from 1/8th ad valorem to 1/16th. A Benjamin Rees was manager. Shortly afterwards there was a further brief item in the Mining Journal naming the Rosebush company, saying that, 'An enormous amount of capital has been sunk a short time ago.' Most of this 'Enormous amount of capital' was the £8000 which Davies and Keylock reputedly received for the lease!

In spite of a firm market, transport costs and royalties meant they were on a loser. They did negotiate with a Josiah Thomas to take over their lease but this fell through and the company would up in 1868.

In 1869 Edward Cropper, a retired Manchester businessman living in Kent heard of the quarry through his step-son Joseph Macaulay who had business interests in the county. In spite of advanced age and ill health he bought the freehold from Mrs Williams for £3750 and bought the plant, such as it was from the receivers of Rosebush Slate for £800.

His purchase of the freehold not only freed him from rent and royalties, but also gave him security of tenure which enabled him to invest freely in infrastructure. With ample means and no shareholders hungry for instant profits he was able to take a long view on such investment, which notably included the Narbeth Road and Maenclochog Railway.

He put Macaulay in charge, assisted by William Pritchard, by now the most experienced manager in the county, whose job at Cronllwyn had just fallen through. Wisely ignoring pre-existing work, an opening was made part-way up the hillside on new ground to the south, working on 4 terraces. All tipping of waste was to the north, good block being taken to the south by tramways on each level. A self-acting incline brought material from levels 1 and 2 down to level 3 and another from 3 to 4. Roofing slate being made on levels 3 and 4.

It was on these upper levels that Macaulay's ingenuity over-rode Pritchard's experience when a windmill was erected apparently to drive dressing machines. The windmill was damaged in a storm before drive-gear could be devised and the dressing machines were never powered.

A further incline lowered finished product to the ground level stock yard and block to a mill which had 4 saws and 3 planers, driven by a Francis water turbine via underfloor shafting. A contemporary report said that 'This machinery did its work famously and required but few hands'.

When working progressed downward below level 4, rubbish was removed via a tunnel on level 5. A tunnel on level 6 drained, carried block to the mill and rubbish to the tip. It also provided an exit for roofing slates made in the pit. Latterly, slates were made in the mill using a treadle operated slate dresser thus forming, albeit in miniature, the only example in south Wales of an Integrated Mill, processing both slab and roofing slate.

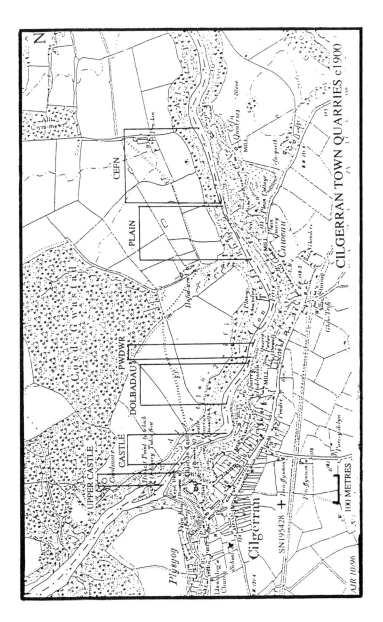

CILGERRAN TOWN QUARRIES c1900

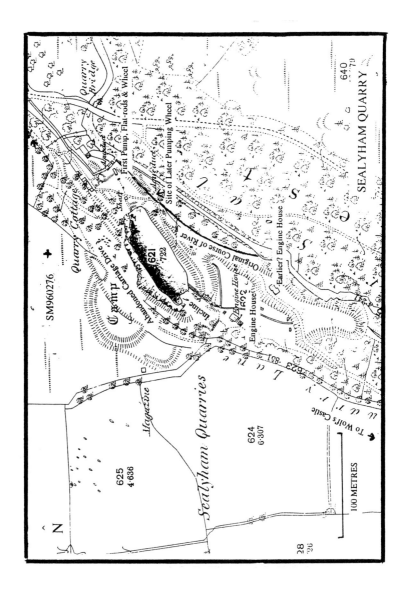

Quarry Bridge

Quarry Cottage

First Pump, Flat-rods & Wheel

Site of Later Pumping Wheel

SM960276

Shaft

Shaft

621
722

Camp Prosceau

Abandoned Incline

Incline

Original Course of River

"Earlier? Engine House

Engine House"

1692

Engine House

SEALYHAM QUARRY

640

N

Magazine

Sealyham Quarries

625
4·636

624
6·307

To Wolf's Castle

523 851

28
26

100 METRES

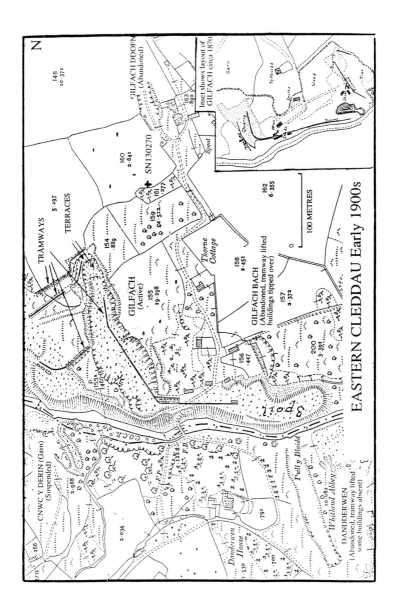

EASTERN CLEDDAU Early 1900s

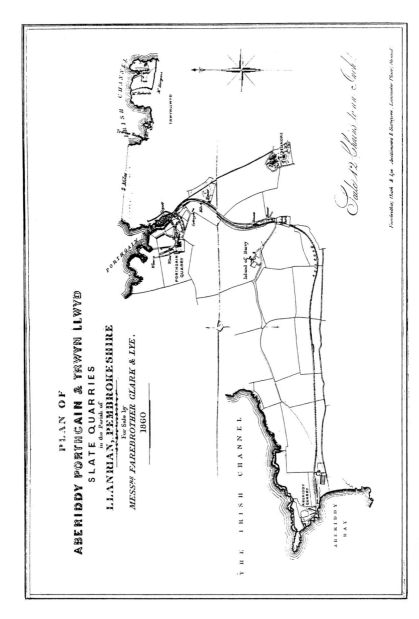

PLAN OF
ABERIDDY PORTHGAIN & TRWYN LLWYD
SLATE QUARRIES
in the Parish of
LLANRIAN, PEMBROKESHIRE
For Sale by
MESSRS FAREBROTHER CLARK & LYE.
1860

Scale 12 Chains to an Inch

PORTHGAIN QUARRY

ABERIDDY QUARRY

ABERIDDY BAY

THE IRISH CHANNEL

Island of Barry

IRISH CHANNEL

TRWYNLLWYD

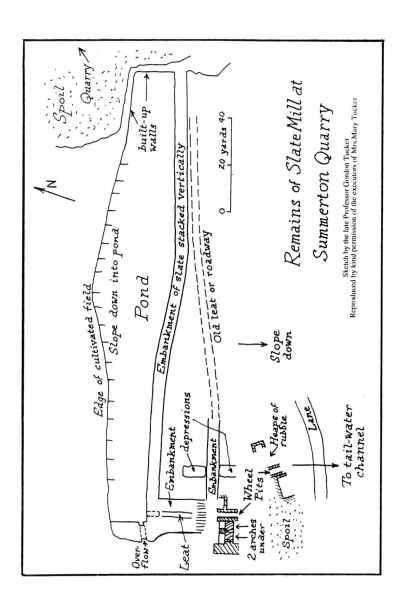

Remains of Slate Mill at Summerton Quarry

Sketch by the late Professor Gordon Tucker
Reproduced by kind permission of the executors of Mrs. Mary Tucker

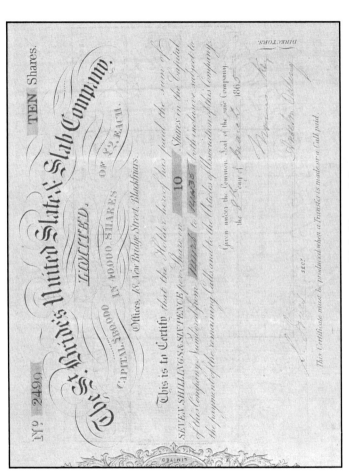

By Courtesy of B.R. Moore & Co.
Antiquarian Share Certificates 01970 871795

Rosebush: Mill and engine shed on either side of
Railway. 6 Adit to left of the mill. 5 Adit to right.
Path to early workings rises to left
Photo: Mr R. Worsley

Gilfach c1956: Quarrying tools including
'Pembrokeshire' saw
Photo: Mr R. Worsley

Gilfach: Posed picture in Dressing Shed c1900s
Photo: Mr R. Worsley

Dolbadau Quarry c1907
Photo: T. Mathias
Courtesy: Scolton Manor Museum

Gilfach: using Pembrokeshire saw 1956
Laurie Owens L, Chris Jenkins R, sadly Chris was killed
in a rockfall shortly afterwards
Photo: Mr R. Worsley

Cefn Mill c1907
Courtesy: Scolton Manor Museum

Cefn Quarry c1907
Courtesy: Scolton Manor Museum

Abereiddi: Lift & Engine House
By kind permission of the
Exors of Prof. Gordon & Mrs Mary Tucker

Plain Quarry Mill – now restored as warehouse
By kind permission of the
Exors of Prof. Gordon & Mrs Mary Tucker

Llandeilo South: Dressing machine now scrapped
By kind permission of the
Exors of Prof. Gordon & Mrs Mary Tucker

Cefn Mill c1907: Saw in foreground, planer behind
Courtesy: Mrs Mary Lewis & the Cilgerran Town Trust

Gilfach 1956: Splitting slate
Photo: Mr R. Worsley

Gilfach 1956: Dressing slate
Photo: Mr R. Worsley

Gilfach c1905: Weighing slate
Photo: Mr R. Worsley

Cefn Mill: Now extended as farm building
Photo: Author

Klondyke Building,
possibly 'Caban' (Hut for eating) with fireplace (turf?)
Photo: Author

Rosebush Mill
Photo: Author

Clyngwyn Dressing Machine: since donated by
Mr J. Wheeler to Welsh Slate Museum, Llanberis
Photo: Author

Fforest Tunnel Tommy Quarry
Photo: Author

Cilgerran Town & Gorge
Photo: Author

Water supply for the mill was obtained by damming the original working, fed by an inverted syphon from Mynydd Du to the north. The tailrace supplied the quarrymen's cottages as well as Macaulay's own house.

In 1878 no less a person than C.E. Spooner (of Ffestiniog Railway fame), was called in to advise on further development. It is a tribute to the soundness of the methods that the only advice he could give was to acquire more tipping ground adjacent to the level 6 tunnel.

The quarry was one of the best planned in Wales and after the opening of the railway, one of the very few able to load directly into standard gauge wagons. Its workforce of well over 100 and its near 5000 ton output dominated the Pembrokeshire scene. The principal product was slab said to have been in sizes up to 7' x 4' x 4". Offcuts were used to make items such as inkstands, letter weights and chessboards, which were sent to Langer, Powell & Magnus at Buckingham Palace Road, London for enamelling.

The 26 cottages which still form Rosebush Terrace, were models of their kind. Though having only one room above the other and a lean-to kitchen, with their slate roofs and flagged floors, they were much superior to the sort of earth-floored hovel that most of the men must have been accustomed to, and let at £2 p.a. were much sought after.

Unfortunately even before the railway opened in 1877, the price of slate which had advanced almost every year since Cropper's purchase, collapsed. Besides which, with the market moving into surplus, buyers became more choosy, opting for the more fashionable north Wales products. Up to the time of his death in 1879 it was estimated that Cropper had spent £22,000 at Rosebush and that his gross revenues had not greatly exceeded a third of that figure.

By 1880 the trade press euphemistically suggested that this quarry 'could do with more trade', as indeed also could the railway. Even at its peak, the quarry's output would have scarcely filled 10 wagons per week. Under-utilised and burdened by the GWR's £500 p.a. charges at Narberth Road (later Clynderwen), the railway closed in 1882. With both price and demand in a steepening downward spiral, Rosebush's brief glory was effectively over.

Edward Cropper's widow Margaret had married landowner Col. John Owen, son of Sir Hugh Owen. They tried to offset the quarry's decline by energetically promoting the health giving properties of the Maenclochog air. They publicised the facilities of Precelly Hotel and put lakes and fountains, (fed by the mill supply) in their own garden to amuse visitors. The visitors may have been amused by the fountains, but the Colonel does not appear to have been amused by the visitors. Shortly after his death in 1890 Margaret wrote quoting him as having said:

'Not one word can be said in favour of them. They cheat the nation, they defraud the Railway Companies of their fares, they bilk the turnpikes. No corn, no hay are wanted, no ostler to be paid, no posting, no coaching required. A pint of beer perhaps the only harvest of the town through which they pass.'

These dreadful parasites were cyclists! Some of them, it was alleged even 'Propped their bicycles against the hotel wall to eat their sandwiches.'

The re-opening of the railway in 1884 failed to restore the quarry's fortunes. Macaulay moved away, Cropper's elder son James was a professional soldier and his younger son Edward took little interest in matters at Rosebush. By 1887 William Pritchard's son Alfred had leased the quarry and moved into the 9 roomed manager's house, with the adjacent village shop being run by his two sisters.

By this time not all the cottages could be let and one was used as an office. Before the end of the '80s the railway had closed again and the quarry was idle. In 1889 an attempt was made to sell them both. There were no takers for the railway and the best that could be done with the quarry was a let at a nominal £1 p.a. as a source of tip material. In 1891 with the market recovering, Pritchard investigated the prospects for a revival. It was estimated that there was a potential for 1300 tons p.a. of roofing slates, 500 tons of slab and 3500 tons of rough block. To produce this would require another tunnel to fully work the 6 levels and a second turbine in the mill would call for doubling up on the supply pipe. With the prospect of this costing £5000 and faced with cartage costs to Fishguard of 15/- (75p) per ton, nothing was done. By 1895 when the railway reopened as the North Pembroke and Fishguard Railway, Pritchard was busy re-opening Gilfach.

Most of the quarry property was now owned by Joseph Rowlands a Birmingham solicitor, although Rosebush Terrace was bought by the Rev. Albert and Mr Walter Hughes.

In the early 1900s the Misses Pritchard were still running the shop, but apart from renting a stable, Pritchard himself had severed all connection. Some desultory work was done until c.1905 by Griffith Williams who rented both Rosebush and Bellstone at £6.5.0 p.a. (£6.25).

There was an amusing episode in 1904 when several women living in Rosebush Terrace, broke fences to extend their gardens onto quarry land. It appears from extant correspondence that Williams found these ladies intimidating neighbours and they may well have precipitated his departure.

In 1908 when this quarry and Bellstone came up for sale, Col. Owen's daughter Edith bought them for £720 with the intention of finding a tenant to work them. She was unsuccessful.

Remains The site abuts Bellstone, the most obvious relic being the pilastered walls of the fine mill building. In one corner the mill is the pit for the water turbine. The ruined loco shed on the other side of the railway trackbed matches the style of the mill. Maps show a subsidiary building to the south of the mill and a range of buildings behind the engine shed, but almost all trace of these has been lost. Also prominent are the abutments of the bridge which carried the tipping line from 5 tunnel over the railway.

On levels 3 and 4 most of the 10 or 12 dressing sheds survive, several paired back-to-back. Where such a layout, rarely seen outside north east Wales, was adopted they were normally of different sizes, the larger being intended for slab dressing, the smaller for roofing slate. These are of identical dimensions suggesting that roofing slate was worked in one or the other according to wind direction.

On the south side of the quarry are the three much degraded inclines.

Both tunnels are open at the quarry ends. However the one on level 6 which emerged on the level is blocked at its outer end. The level 5 tunnel has a nice arch at its outer end but being partly through waste is supported by crossbars and props of light railway rails which have collapsed at one point.

There is a partly flooded tunnel entering the working face at level 4 which may have been a pre-existing metal mine. Above level 1 there is some trial working.

All trace of the windmill on the hill above has been obliterated by forestry. At level 2, cut by the workings, is a leat which may have been an early water supply.

The access track to the original (pre Cropper) working is prominent and the pit still holds water. Some pipework is visible, both here and up valley to the north. Some distances away on the flat ground to the west, a powder house survives.

The houses of Rosebush Terrace, along the rail line to the quarry, are still occupied, several with the original slates on the roofs. At the end is the manager's house, now a cafe, and abutting is the Misses Pritchard's shop. Local legend has it that their customers were required to drop their coins through a hole in the counter into a basin of water, so that they were cleaned before the ladies handled them. Since 1972 the dwellings have been on mains water, a matter of complaint at the time as apart from having to pay, the occupiers complained that the public supply was inferior to the quarry water.

The corrugated iron Precelly Hotel, now renamed 'Tafarn Sinc' is still very much in business and the station partly reconstructed. Mr Gareth Williams, besides restoring the water gardens has at last, with his caravan park, succeeded in promoting the area as a tourist destination. Mr Williams' grandfather Griffith Williams was the quarry's maintenance man. When he took up his appointment he walked from Porthgain having sailed there from Porthmadog which he had reached by walking from Aberdaron.

PANTMAENOG SN080313
Small hillside quarry.
Remains Slot-like excavation. Adjacent are small reservoirs which formed part of the Rosebush supply. Also traces of tiny working at 080314.

TREBENGYCH SN073281
Tiny, worked presumably only at intervals from the 1830s or before, to c.1880/1890.
Remains Shallow excavation.

VAGUR SN096284
A small working on either side of the road, originally known as Hafod Ddu. Landlord George Le Hunte leased it to William Knell and John Davies in 1866, at a rent of £30 p.a.,. merging to a royalty of 1/16th. Thomas Nicholas, late of Dandderwen was manager. They gave up in 1869. Thomas Nicholas was running it in 1877 as well as overseeing Penlan for William Bishop. It is not clear if he was the lessee of Vagur or was acting for Bishop.

This may have been the 'Maenclochog' quarry which J.A. Hesford was working circa 1912. It was working immediately post-WW1, as John Williams a casual worker of Penrhos recorded in his diary in 1919, 'drove slates from Vagwr'.

Remains To north of the road, heavily overgrown, to the south, partly filled in.

Area 4 The Eastern Cleddau

Most of the quarries in this compact area worked a volcanic ash slate, akin to English Lake District material and quite unlike the argillaceous mudstone slate of other Welsh quarries.

Almost all are very small, a few are ancient but most date from the latter part of the 19th century when the G.W.R. enabled the uniqueness of their 'Green' slate to be exploited as a speciality material in English markets.

Although many had only a brief existence, some such as Gilfach and Tyrch were particularly successful in developing and maintaining a niche market at premium prices up to WW2 and beyond.

Had the quarries been able to reap benefits of scale by amalgamation and had any of the once proposed branch railways been built, this area might have become a substantial producer.

SN098272	Temple Druid *
104272	etc. Llandeilo *
105270	Llandeilo South *
106265	Noble Court
108268	Teilo Vale
110262	Lily *
112272	Llyn
115265	Llangolman Farm
119264	Pencraig
124260	Clyngwyn *
126269	Dandderwen
126272	Cnwc y Derin
128271	Gilfach *
129262	Llwyn yr Ebol *
145294	Tyrch *
167300	Klondyke *

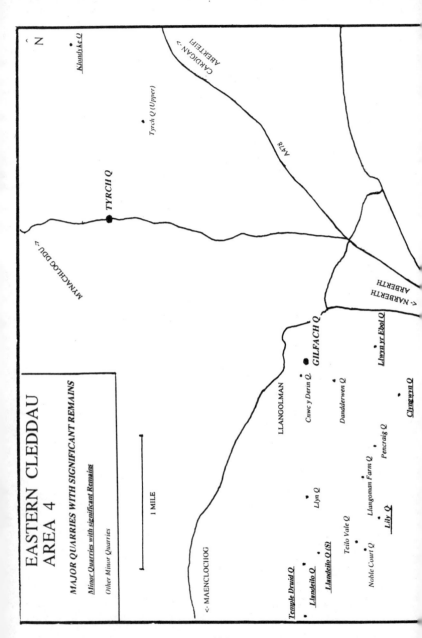

EASTERN CLEDDAU
AREA 4

MAJOR QUARRIES WITH SIGNIFICANT REMAINS

Minor Quarries with significant Remains

Other Minor Quarries

1 MILE

N

Klondyke Q

Tyrch Q (Upper)

TYRCH Q

MYNACHLOG DDU →

CARDIGAN →
ABERTEIFI

A478

← NARBERTH ARBERTH

GILFACH Q

Cnwc y Derin Q

LLANGOLMAN

Dandderwen Q

Llwyn yr Ebol Q

Clyngwyn Q

Pencraig Q

Llyn Q

Llangoman Farm Q

Teilo Vale Q

Lily Q

← MAENCLOCHOG

Temple Druid Q

Llandeilo Q

Llandeilo Q (S)

Noble Court Q

104

CLYNGWYN SN124260

A hillside quarry worked on a moderate scale, probably discontinuously, during the mid 19th century. It is not clear if it was included in the tract taken by the Cleddau Valley Slate Quarries Company 1877-80, but it appears to have been worked at that time. In 1883 it was reported in the press that 'Arrangements are being made to work Clyngwyn on a more extensive scale', and some work was done following this.

Operations were revived in 1928 by the Wheeler family (who still farm the adjacent land). Employing redundant Glogue men, they at first sold over 25000 slates p.a. A few were up to 20 x 10 @ about £19 per 1000, but most were Randoms and Locals at prices down to under £5. By 1931 sales had fallen to 6000, averaging little over 1000 p.a. to 1938 closure.

Remains Three extraction sites. The larger of the two lower areas is just a quarrying face, the smaller and older has traces of a pair of early dressing sheds. The upper area, where the last extraction occurred, has a rake of three tiny shelters, two of which housed treadle powered Greaves pattern dressing machines, made by Turner of Newtown of an unusual single bladed type, widely used in the eastern Cleddau area but rare elsewhere. One of these was donated by Mr Jeff Wheeler to the Welsh Slate Museum in 1996, but fragments of the other remain on site. It is believed that three were bought from Gilfach, but one was smashed in transit.

An incline with traces of a sheave mounting at its head connects the two larger levels. Below near the river, is a powder store built into the rock. The access tracks are much overgrown.

CNWC Y DERIN (Garn, West Gilfach) SN126272

Two adjacent workings, mid 19th century or possibly much earlier. Operated by the Lily Quarries Slate & Slab Co. from

1866 to 1868 and jointly managed with Lily by James Charles. J.R. Price rented it in 1873 for £20 p.a. When the freehold changed hands 3 years later the veins were described as being of, 'Very superior Slate and Flag' and described as 'Lying in close proximity to the Celebrated Gilfach Slate Quarry on the opposite side of the river'. In 1880 Price was said to have been making 'nice slates' but it was dormant when John Absalom took it in 1908.

Absalom adopted the style 'Whitland Abbey Green Slate' which Gilfach had just abandoned in favour of 'Precelly Green'. As well as the original two adjacent workings, a new opening was made at 127270, but this was not successful.

After WW1 closure it was restarted by John Absalom's son Glyn as Garn Green & Rustic Slate Quarries Co where in the immediate post-war years his 'Welsh Artistic Slates' met a number of substantial contracts.

After WW2 work continued on diminishing scale until 1954 when Glyn Absalom merged it with Gilfach as Pembrokeshire Slates Ltd. Though now dormant and the treadle dressing machines scrapped, Glyn's son, Mr J.D. Absalom, still supplies block for sculptural and decorative uses using a portable disc cutter.

Remains A long cutting plus a smaller working, evidence of tramways to extensive tips. Little trace of buildings other than a modern temporary structure. The 127270 excavation is much overgrown.

DANDDERWEN *(Whitland Abbey, Tan y Dderwen)* SN126269 & 127268

The early history and the date of opening of these two adjoining diggings which included both 'Green' and 'Blue' veins is unclear, but 127268 or Lower Dandderwen was almost certainly working in the 18th century and possibly before that. It was let by a D. Hughes in 1863 to John Davies, H. Ledgard and others, at a £75 p.a. dead rent with no royalty. Curiously the lease stated that the rent would be reduced to £50 if the quality of the slate was not found to be 'Equal or better than Abereiddi'. (!)

The following year they leased the Upper, flag, quarry from Joseph Thomas at a rent of £200 p.a. (half rent for the first year). The vein was said to be small but capable of yielding a good quality slab.

Perhaps because Davies had yet to discover that selling quarries was more profitable than working them, the syndicate seems to have operated them without attempting to float a company. It cannot have lasted long since by 1866 their manager Thomas Nicholas had moved to Vagur. As the advertisement of 1868 shows, John Muscott had by then taken over and on the strength of slates unearthed in 1855 on the site of Whitland Abbey being identified as of Eastern Cleddau origin, was pushing the rather tenuous connection.

SLATES AND PAVING
The Whitland Abbey Slate Co have always on sale at their wharf at Narberth Road station a quantity of their green and blue slate slab, good durable paving at 2/6 (12½p) per yard. For particulars apply to Mr John Muscott, Cilfaufawr Narberth.

Muscott was succeeded by his son, John junior who having rented the Dandderwen estate ran both workings, expanding the Upper, laying an appreciable run of internal tramway. He successfully pioneered the marketing of the eastern Cleddau Green slate as a premium price speciality product becoming the leading producer. By 1876 he was publishing a price list:

WHITLAND ABBEY GREEN SLATES

24 x 12	400/-	(£20)	90cwt	1100 ft
22 x 12	330/-	(£15.50)	80 cwt	950 ft
20 x 10	220/-	(£11.50)	60 cwt	775 ft
18 x 10	175/-	(£8.75)	54 cwt	675 ft
18 x 9	155/-	(£7.75)	50 cwt	600 ft

16 x 10	155/-	(£7.75)	50 cwt	600 ft
16 x 8	110/-	(£5.50)	35 cwt	475 ft
14 x 8	80/-	(£4)	30 cwt	400 ft
14 x 7	65/-	(£3.25)	25 cwt	350 ft
12 x 8	55/-	(£2.75)	25 cwt	350 ft
12 x 7	45/-	(£2.25)	22 cwt	300 ft
12 x 6	35/-	(£1.75)	18 cwt	250 ft

Delivered free into trucks at Clynderwen station 7/ per ton
Railway rate to Paddington 13/4 per ton

These prices per mil of 1200 approximated to north Wales Bests, but were four times the weight, thus cartage of 35p and carriage 67p, added £4.50 per mil to the London cost of the largest size. The claimed coverage, incidentally was for the usual 3" lap.

In 1883 in spite of the dull market Muscott interested five Swansea businessmen and J.R. Bishop of Pembroke in floating Whitland Abbey Slate as a limited company with an authorised capital of £25,000. To strengthen his hand he had a number of reports made which differ from the usual 'reports' as they seem to have been made by genuinely independent persons. The one produced by David Smith a Birmingham engineer strongly criticised the transport arrangements –

'I find your cost of Carriage by Horse Teams to the Great Western Railway, amounts to £0.17s.6d (87.5p) per thousand upon your principal size 20-in. by 10-in. This charge so materially adds to the cost of these Green Slates as to prevent in many cases their adoption in preference to other Green Slates of inferior quality.'

He went on to suggest a 3 mile railway to the Maenclochog Railway, stating that –

'The cost of carriage will be reduced by fifteen shillings (75p) per thousand on your 20-in. by 10-in. size. And further, it will also prevent a breakage occasioned by unloading, reloading and breakage in transit to the G.W. R. amounting to 5 per cent, or a total saving of '£1.5s.0d. (£1.25) per thousand.'

Considering the state of roads at the time, a few miles in a cart producing a 5% breakage was not unreasonable. However his claim that '3130 thousand' slates had been produced in two years working was less credible, inferring an annual output of around 4000 tons, not counting slab. He stated that the river could provide 80 hp of water power for –

'Raising slates, sawing window sills, chimney pieces, facings for windows and doorways, and especially corner stones for buildings.'

In addition to the mention of power, a tunnel was also recommended, 'To drain the large Blue Vein and the two large Green Veins'. This inferred pit working, which could not have gone to any great depth as even the upper quarry was only a few feet above river level.

Costs of the machinery, turbine etc. were estimated to be £2,500 and the railway £7,500, with £3,000 required for working capital.

Smith put some emphasis on 'Corner Stones' as an intended mainstream product. This may have been a perception that more of such items were needed for a building than sills and so on, or it may have suggested that he had no great opinion of the slab quality. However there were several testimonials to the durability of the products. The Rev. R.B. Jones, Vicar of Killymaenllwryd said that there was a monument in his churchyard dated 1769 with the letters 'as distinct and clear and unaffected by weather or climate as if they had been cut a few months ago', adding that 18th century stones were also to be seen at Henllan and Glanrhyd. Others included a letter stating that the slates on Gloucester Asylum, '– give entire satisfaction'. Another from a merchant referring to slates for Keble College Oxford was more guarded saying 'We have heard no complaint of quality'. A correspondent spoke of those on Camrose church, 'They look well and pleased me very much'. Others praised roofs on Abergavenny and Avebury churches. Yet another said that 'To my mind the Green colour is infinitely superior to the ordinary Blue slate; and I must add that the roof of my house is greatly admired'. Quaintly, it was said of a Pelcombe Architect that, 'He likes them thick'.

Little is known about the company's activities, other than that John Muscott acted as manager. They should have picked up business from Gilfach which was going through a bad patch but were clearly in serious trouble in January 1886 when Muscott wrote to C.E.G. Philips of Picton Castle.

> I take the liberty of informing you that I have reduced the price of these Green Slates by 40% bringing them down to the level of North Wales Slates, whilst the latter are brought to our very doors (for instance to Maenclochog Mill), our own men are starving and our local trade ruined. Of course I know you have a perfect right to use what Slates you may think proper, I believe that if you could be convinced you could have an article of local production as good as anything you could get elsewhere, you would instantly give that the preference, and thereby increase your popularity. Well, I can fearlessly tell you that I can supply you with this article, and I do hope you will kindly give me some support this year. I also have large quantities of first class Window Sills and Slabs, Corner Stones &c. Trusting you will excuse my writing direct to you.

To have been asking two thirds above north Wales prices suggests a robust optimism on Mr Muscott's part and that he was quite out of touch with the extent the market had fallen over the previous eight or nine years. It is no wonder that Mr Philips was going elsewhere for slate for his estate!

The company was wound up the following year with none of Smith's suggestions for transport or power implemented. When shortly afterwards, the freehold of Dandderwen farm was sold, the Lower quarry was described as having four buildings, the largest being without a roof.

In 1890 with the market improving, Muscott and his brother George reopened but they faced both increasing competition and working difficulties. They continued on a diminishing scale for a few years before offering the quarry for sale. It was bought by Alfred Pritchard in 1896 who may have sold it on to John Absalom in 1908, but almost certainly neither worked it.

Remains Lower quarry is just a face with little trace of buildings. Upper quarry is very much larger, gently sloping into a pit as the gradual north westerly dip of the veins was followed, rendering overburden removal increasingly onerous. The working is dry but no drainage tunnel has been located. Nor, due to the site being so heavily overgrown, has it been possible to determine if there is any evidence of the several small buildings which maps show. There is a small subsidiary face at 125268 which was possibly the site of the earliest work. Although it is believed that sandsaws may have been used at one time, all sawn ends found are hand toothed-sawn.

GILFACH (Llangolman) SN128271

By far the largest and most successful of the eastern Cleddau quarries which reputedly dates from the 16th century. Slate from this area was shipped from the nearby Blackpool quay at that time but it cannot be specifically linked to this quarry. It is claimed that it supplied some of the roofing when the Houses of Parliament were rebuilt in the 1830s.

It may have been idle when it was leased in the mid 1860s by a Mr Goodwin, a Whitland architect. It was said in 1866 that a 'tough, durable slate' was being produced which, it was dubiously claimed, 'fetched nearly double North

Wales prices'. It clearly flourished, the early workings near the river bank being abandoned and development made eastward, with a tramway from the working to the river bank where dressing sheds and other buildings were erected. There was also a subsidiary working, Bach, a little to the south which also had buildings and a short tramway.

In 1875 a dispute over tipping on adjacent Garn land indicates it was then being worked by W.H. Yelverton, but by the late 1870s it had succumbed to the slate slump and rail-borne competition. The press reported in late 1880 that Gilfach was 'now changing hands, with a view to working on a large scale and constructing a railway to the Maenclochog Railway 4 miles distant, for which wayleases have been obtained'. This reference is obscure but might indicate that moves were being made by Muscott of Dandderwen, as it is believed that his Whitland Abbey Company of 1883 did take an interest in this site. By 1890 the quarry had been inactive for some time and the lease was for sale.

In 1896 with the slate market improving, but Rosebush being beyond hope of revival, Alfred Pritchard bought the lease, relaid the rails, installed dressers (probably from Rosebush) and reopened with some of his ex-Rosebush men. In spite of the rock being slightly different on this, the Carmarthen side of the river, he hijacked the name 'Whitland Abbey Green Slate Quarries', from the then moribund Dandderwern.

Pritchard's aunt had married into the Davies family of Porthmadog. His cousins, Jonathan and Richard Davies trading as Davies Bros. were large and influential slate merchants as well as having interests in several Blaenau quarries, so it was natural that Pritchard should seek their help in peddling his wares.

The Davies' produced a price list which was boldly if somewhat inaccurately headed

The ORIGINAL and only GENUINE Whitland Abbey Green Slates. From the Old Whitland Abbey quarry recently re-opened.

The 1897 list carried a range of 18 sizes from 24 x 12 down to 10 x 6, but only 6 (24 x 12, 22 x 12, 22 x 11, 20 x 12, 14 x 10 & 11 x 7) were actually being made. They were stated to be of a 'Four to the inch' thickness which would place them something between north Wales 'Mediums' and 'Seconds', but they were asking F.O.R. Llanglydwen, for 24 x 12 for instance, 340/- (£17) and for 11 x 7, 55/- (2.75) approaching what north Wales 'Bests' were then fetching. Unlike most other quarries in the region, no Locals were listed.

The back of the list showed over 40 buildings ranging from Carmarthen Asylum to the Warden's house, Keble College, Oxford and including Mansions, Schools, Railway stations and Churches as far away as Felixstowe, all allegedly roofed with his quarry's material. The list also stated that the quarry had been 'Worked for 400 years'.

Helped by the slate shortage which developed in the closing years of the century, Davies Bros' efforts were an immediate success even at these high prices and within a year they undertook to buy the entire production at discounted prices on a sliding scale related to the annual Porthmadog list. Jonathan Davies took a share in the quarry and assisted both financially and in person with its development, living in makeshift accommodation on site.

Extraction was concentrated at Goodwin's east face, which as the floor advanced downward was accessed and drained by a tunnel. The tramway track was extended south to a tipping ground well clear of any possible expansion. Some further track was laid, but much handling was by wheelbarrow.

Slates were trimmed with treadle operated dressers. Since there was a minimum of slab production there was no call for mechanical saws or planers.

By the early 1900s the 'Whitland Abbey' name having been dropped. 'Precelly Green', was a well established speciality product. Additional skilled labour was found by recruiting from among Penrhyn men made idle by the 1900-1903 stoppage there. Two galleries were developed, each with tramways, and by 1906 60 men were producing well over 2000 tons p.a.

In 1907 Davies Bros., now headed by Jonathan's son Ithel, won the contract for the supply and laying of slates for Bangor University. The architect having specified 'South Wales' slate, Gilfach material was offered. This caused a storm of protest, which was understandable since several Caernarfonshire quarry owners and indeed the north Wales quarrymen themselves, many of whom were by now unemployed, had contributed generously to the college's foundation. Davies Bros. wishing to avoid antagonising their north Wales suppliers, were minded to withdraw, but incensed by allegations of poor quality of Gilfach product made by the north Wales producers, went ahead with the contract.

The furore, which rumbled on for years, was widely reported in the London press. This publicity made 'Precelly Green Slates', now registered as a Trademark, nationally known, and resulted in slate from this hitherto obscure hole in the ground being specified for a number of prestigious buildings throughout Britain.

Unfortunately the benefit was not immediate, and in fact in 1908 tonnage was down to little more than 1000 and manning had to be cut to 49.

By 1910 sales of 'Sized' slates had been abandoned, all being offered in Lake District style as Randoms and Peggies. Sold by the ton in mixed widths, they were classified in lots according to maxium and minimum length. 'Green' slates were classified as Light, Dark, Bright, Olive & Khaki, graded as 'Best' and 'Second Bests'. Slates of mixed colour were sold as 'Rustics'. Slates of ¼" thickness were called 'Ordinary

Thickness', those of 3/8", 'Specially Thick'. F.O.R. prices ranged from 87/6 (£4.37) per ton down to 45/-. This move out of 'Sizes' not only gave a substantially enhanced revenue per ton, but also reduced slate making costs. This undoubtedly helped them to ride out the continuing bad times which by 1912, cut output further and saw manning down to 35.

In 1913 trade picked up, prices were advanced by over 10%, but before the recovery had fully taken hold, the outbreak of war in 1914 led to a collapse into closure.

In 1919, Pritchard and Davies reopened, forming the Precelly Green and Rustic Slate Company with a capital of £5,000. They sold the quarry to the new company for £2,100. Davies had the controlling interest which, following Pritchard's death shortly afterwards, became sole ownership.

In the immediate post WW1 years when even Pembrokeshire County Council was rejecting the local product as too costly, Gilfach was awarded several lucrative contracts by Government Departments. These included, in 1919 60 tons of Rustic Peggies 8" to 12" long for the Guildford Housing Scheme.

Davies successfully rode out the 1922 slump which followed the post-war boom and in 1925 bought Gilfach Ddofn farm, ridding the company of royalties. This gave it ownership of the tiny Gilfach Ddofn digging but it was not worked. Later that year P.F. Campbell who was now working Tyrch quarry, offered to buy Gilfach, but he wisely jibbed at Davies' £16,000 estimate of its worth.

By now strict adherence to Lake District classifications had been abandoned, all roofing product being sold as 'Randoms', but still priced in numbered groups according to maximum and minimum sizes. 'Green' slates were classed as 'Bests', 'Second Bests' and 'Stout'. The latter term being appropriate as they were ¾" thick!

Throughout the 20s & 30s almost 30 men were kept in steady employment and although they only produced around

700 tons p.a., almost every year showed a modest profit. A record that very few other quarries could match.

In 1931 a haulage incline powered by a Commer lorry engine replaced the tunnel access to the main working, the tunnel remaining as a drain. Fuel for the engine and a portable air compressor were almost the only non-wage outgoings apart from cartage to Llanglydwen station. For this, one contractor with a lorry was paid by the ton/mile, the other up to 1936, had a team of two horses, on a daily retainer of 12/- (almost as much as Hugh Hughes, the Manager was earning!)

Not having a blacksmith, the men sharpened their own tools and Hughes had difficulty in getting them to correctly re-form cruciform bits for the pneumatic drill. In 1936, in apparent desperation, a bit was sent to Oakeley quarry in Blaenau Ffestiniog for sharpening. Oakeley charged 13/8 (68p) plus 1/3 (6p) carriage (and added 1/ (5p) to the bill for telephone calls!)

At this time their promotional literature named over one hundred public buildings roofed with Precelly slates and cited as customers, government agencies, local authorities and banks.

By 1939, when many prestigious quarries had fallen into bankruptcy, Ithel Davies still maintained a steady and modestly profitable pace as virtually the sole south Wales producer. His payroll of 39 was only exceeded by about a score of slate quarries in the whole country, a remarkable achievement, particularly when using technology little changed from that of the 18th century. It is also remarkable that in the late 1930s, Davies was able to retain his workforce in competition with better paid and lighter work at Trecwn Armaments Depot.

Production ceased in 1940, but sales continued from stock and from neighbouring closed quarries such as Tyrch, selling the Best Randoms at up to £10 per ton. In 1941 they bought (for £30) Tyrch's two saw tables and a saw sharpening machine, but declined to buy either of the two oil engines offered. It appears that the saws were never installed.

In 1947, Ithel Davies having died, the quarry including a cottage and a manager's house was bought by Mr Plosker a Swansea Draper. He did not work it and in 1954 Glyn Absalom took over and incorporated it with his Pembroke Slates operation at Cnwc y Derin.

Using a fork truck and digger, he produced roofing slate which was trimmed with a Lister powered dressing machine. Other unpowered dressers were on site but not normally used. A second Lister generated 110v electricity to power the disc cutter used for sawing slab. Contracts were secured for several important buildings, including the Victoria & Albert Museum and Aberystwyth University as well as the Grogedda Plant Breeding Station and the Esso refinery at Milford Haven. Slab for ornamental and sculptural purposes was also produced as well as fireplaces etc. One of their last major contracts before disposing of the site in 1987 was for cladding the control room, valve tower and entrance way for the Llys y Frân reservoir.

The quarry is now in the hands of an owner who bought it mainly for his own private use.

Remains The early riverside operation has been tipped over and bulk worked. The newer site to the north east comprises a lofty face, deepened into a pit, having some evidence of gallery working with rubbish runs off. There are vestiges of the tunnel and at the head of the incline which superseded it, is the base for the haulage engine. There are the formations of several tramways, which as in most small quarries, never entirely displaced wheelbarrows.

Nearby is an office and a CGI machinery building and also the ruins of a smithy. There are traces of other buildings including dressing sheds.

A few years to the south is the little Bach pit, now blocked by subsequent tipping which covers the site of its buildings and most of the short tramway. The little Gilfach

Ddofn pit at 132270 has been filled. At 128266 is a tiny riverside working, Cwar Glas, about which nothing is known.

Up to c1990 there was a short length of 6' gauge track in the dressing area. Whilst it would be highly speculative to identify this as the remains of a powered sandsaw, the ditch which skirts the southernmost tips, is shown on a mid 19th century map as 'Tailrace for watercourse', which gives rise to the possibility of power sawing having been used at an early date.

KLONDYKE (Dolmaen, Dolemaen, Foel) SN167300

Small pit, probably worked intermittently during the 19th century and possibly earlier. Several attempts were made from c1900 to develop it and in 1908 the geological report made by Professor W. Galloway of Cardiff for H.L. Lewis who was then about to take over Tyrch, included this site. He was of the opinion that the vein extended continuously across the mountain and was in fact better here than at Tyrch. The following year, Lewis only having taken Tyrch Lower, a report was commissioned, on this and Tyrch Upper from G.B. Thomas, who had been at Tyrch and was then managing Cefn (Cilgerran).

After the usual preliminaries that the rock was 'Inexhaustible' he suggested that a number of new openings be made and that up to 150 men could be employed. Costs would be low as there was already a drainage tunnel at Foel and 'Rough labour can be obtained at low figures'. He mentioned having seen slab 'manufactured from the rock obtained therefrom – which should find ready sale for high class residences'. Puzzingly is his reference to such slab as being planed as there were no planing machines in the area.

The Dolmaen Silver Grey Slate Co. was formed in 1910 with an authorised capital of £25,000, by A.O. Evans a retired Architect and J.E. Spickett a solicitor, both from Pontypridd. Having bought a considerable tract of land for probably about £2,000, they proposed selling it to the company for £10,000 in cash and £5,000 in shares.

They predicted that within six months they could produce 15,000 slates per week, fetching a total of some £136. Splitting wages would be about £39. 350 tons of rock would be needed costing £17.10.0 (£17.50) to win and 100 tons of overburden removal would cost £3.15.0 (£3.75), management and overheads would amount to £11.15.0 (£11.75), leaving a weekly profit of £64 plus an estimated nett return on other products of £12. Cartage to the station, charged to the customer, would be 3/6 (17.5p).

In spite of this attractive return which would give a dividend of at least 10%, there were few if any takers. The company idea was abandoned and they went ahead as a partnership, with the involvement of G. Davies and J. Williams of Pontypridd who were opening up at Teilo Vale.

They published a full list of prices of roofing slates in 1912 describing them as 'Tyrch Vein, Light or Silver Grey'. Against the local trend they listed Sized slates, from 20 x 10 @ £11.15.0 (£11.75) per mil of 1200, down to 14 x 7 @ £4.15.3 (£4.76) Free on Rail at Crymmach Arms station.

E. Mathews their selling agent for south east England must have had a task to get orders for these as the prices were in the order of a third above Ffestiniog Bests. Besides which, their 20 x 10s for instance weighed 67 cwt per mil, almost three times north Wales Bests. Thus their rail carriage to London @ 13/1 (65.4p) per ton cost over £2 per mil, whereas north Wales product could be got there for under £1 and even less by ship. Correspondence suggests that they were prepared to shade list prices, but so was everyone else at this time.

Their prices for 'Lake District' slates which ranged from 74/ (£3.70) per ton down to 47/- (£2.35), were highly competitive, appreciably below the going rate in the locality. These were offered as Randoms and Peggies in 3 thicknesses as well as Rustics. Their A grade were declared as 'Ordinary thickness', B as 'Averaging 3/8" Substance' and C as 'Specially thick 3/8" and Upwards'.

These gave them their sole large order, for the roofing of the Glamorgan County Council offices at Cardiff.

They also offered Damp Course slates, then a relatively new product. These were listed at 25/ (£1.25) per ton, about on a par with north Wales.

The quarry was reported as idle at the end of 1912.

Remains Narrow flooded excavation. Extensive rubbish runs, (one had bridge under), collapsed drainage tunnel, vestige of possible forge and powder house.

LILY SN110262

Also sometimes called Llangolman, it was a substantial hillside working with 2 galleries.

In 1865 John Davies formed the £15,000 Lily Quarries Slate and Slab Co., persuading J.R. Armitage, Thomas Key, W.W. Staples and John Scott to subscribe. It was stated that £5 shares could be secured for 10/- (50p) deposit with a further 10/- payable on allotment, with the final total not expected to exceed £3.10.0 (£3.50).

Davies had naturally first obtained the 21 year lease on the 120 acres which included a tiny quarry then known as Parc. He pointed out when selling it to the company for £7,000, half in cash, half in shares, that it was 'Without rent and at the extremely favourable royalty of one sixteenth'. He appointed himself and Ledgard directors.

He claimed that the quarry had 'Three well-known veins only partially opened which produces Slate and Slab of the largest dimensions. The Roofing Slate is of peculiar description only found in this particular neighbourhood, the same textured slate as Gilfach, now much in demand'. He described the rock as 'greenish blue with silvery threads', and similar to that which had recently 'roofed the Whitehall house of the Duke of Buccleuch, the newly embellished Guildhall and Charing Cross Hotel and Station'.

Elsewhere he claimed that the slate 'Sells at fully double the price of the best blue slate. The few quarries in the locality have a monopoly which exceeds supply'. Later naming these as Gilfach, Dandderwen and Cnwc y Derin who were, he alleged, 'Yielding a profit of 50% to 100%' and going on to say that Gilfach was 'The most successful quarry in Wales, fast followed by Dandderwen'(!)

He estimated that the river could supply up to three 40' water wheels and could drive saws and planers which would cost £4,000. He said men could be had for 1/8 (7p) per day and boys for 6d to 1/- (2.5p – 5p), these wages being 'Half that of northern districts'.

It apparently was costing 5/- and 6/- per ton respectively to send output the 5 miles to Narberth Road or the 7 miles to Fishguard, but it was said that 'When the tramroad is constructed the cost will be 1/4 (6.7p) as well as speeding shipment at Haverfordwest or Milford'. It was also claimed that the holding was large enough to sell or sub-let a portion. On the strength of this he guaranteed a dividend of 5% for the first year, 7½% the second and 20% for the third.

James Charles the manager here as well as at Cnwc y Derin was reported as saying, 'I venture to state that by May next there will not be a better property in Wales for its extent'. The press reported an 'extraordinary demand' for the product. Davies, Charles and the press, were of course all wrong and the company ceased work after three years. There may have been some further working up to c1890.
Remains Traces of dressing sheds and of ends cut with toothed hand-saws. There is a possible leat but no evidence of water power actually having been used. The now muddy track through to Llangolman farm may have been built by the company. There is a much overgrown trial at 108265.

LLANDEILO SN104272 (etc.)
The original working (Chwarel Glas) was at 103276, with a further tiny site at 103277. There was a small

mill/workshop building. J.R. Bishop may have been the lessee in the mid 1870s.

The largest working at 104272 is probably a mid 1895 redevelopment by the Muscott brothers of Dandderwen, George being the owner and John the manager. John died in 1908 when they were employing 9 men. George carried on intermittently up to WW1, suffering several falls of rock and, most oddly, a strike in 1914. Although aged 85, he re-opened in 1919 working on and off until January 1926.

Remains The working immediately north of the road is flooded. The mill/workshop is in reuse as a dwelling. There are the abutments of a bridge over the road and several dressing-shed type structures. There is a 60m long tunnel, the purpose of which is unclear. At the two smaller workings, faces only.

LLANDEILO SOUTH SN105270

Rather larger than the neighbouring Llandeilo quarries. John Davies had an interest in 1864 when it was referred to, undoubtedly by him, as experiencing 'Extraordinary demand'.

J.R. Price was operating it in 1870, but apparently it had been closed for some time when W. Melchoir took it in 1891. In 1912 it was trading as Llandilo Green Slate Quarries with 19 men. Some work was done up to the 1950s, with wheelbarrows still supplementing the rail track.

Remains Long, narrow quarry, working area building now demolished but a fine loading platform is extant. Nearby are derelict cottages and other buildings. There was a dressing machine on site for many years which was of the same pattern as the Clyngwyn machines, but with the original safety screen replaced by the mesh enclosure which later regulations required. The treadle had been removed suggesting it was powered by an i.c. engine, but anecdotal accounts say that there was no power on site and all dressers were foot-operated.

Sawn ends on the tips are hand-sawn.

LLANGOLMAN FARM *(Chwarel Fawr)* SN115265

A small pit. Presumably had been in use well before it was leased by John Davies from John Phillips in 1864 for £50 p.a. plus 1/16th royalty. Davies sold the lease to Lily Quarries Slate & Slab Co. the next year but it is not clear if they worked it.

When the farm was offered for sale in 1888, the presence was mentioned of a 'Green slate formation, a continuation of the Gilfach vein celebrated for its durability and colour', but there was no suggestion that it was active.

Owned and possibly worked, early 20th century by a Mr Thomas.

Remains Overgrown pit.

LLWYN YR EBOL SN129262 & 127260

A small riverside working and a larger hillside working, on the southern limit of the Green slate occurrences. They were long established serving a local clientele when they were leased in 1877 by William Bishop, a Bristol man living at Llanboidy, who was also involved in quarrying at Penlan and Pencelli in the Tâf valley. He immediately formed the Cleddau Valley Slate Quarries Company, the preliminary press announcement in June of that year saying –

Subscriptions are invited for £12,000 in the Cleddau valley slate quarries. Two veins are of Green slate realising £20 per 1000 in Whitland Abbey quarries adjoining. Labour is abundant, more so than in north Wales. The lease is for 40 years unexpired with no royalty at a rent of £65 per annum.

The Blue slate is of first rate quality and well situated for working. There is ample water power for all purposes of machinery necessary for the extensive development of the quarries. They will be worked by open galleries one above the other thereby unwatering themselves. Rubbish will be tipped down from each gallery and it is mentioned that the slate being good and marketable almost to the very surface, a large amount will be saved in the development of the works.

It must be bourne in mind that no delay will take place in making this a productive property as immediately upon the company's taking on and working the quarry profits will commence and increase with rapidity as works progress.

Situate 4 miles from Clynderwen station on the Great Western & South Wales Union Railway. It is proposed to lay a railway to make a junction with the Clynderwen and Maenclochog Railway, 3 miles distant.'

Apart from the somewhat exaggerated estimate of the Whitland Abbey (Dandderwen) prices, they could produce little of its 'Green' slate, their rock being mainly argillaceous, yielding 'Blue' slate. This, apart from fetching lower prices, was facing increasing competition from the north Wales producers who had just announced what was to prove the first of seven annual price cuts.

The capitalisation was for £24,000 in shares and £15,000 in debentures. Terms offered to investors were unusual and suspiciously generous. Buyers of shares were 'assured of a divident of 10% for 3 years, secured on Government Securities' (?). The £12,000 of debentures which were offered were described as being 'secured on the assets' (??), were to carry 10% interest and be redeemable by the company at £110%, for which purpose a sinking fund would be established. Buyers of such debentures were to receive a bonus in shares amounting to 50% of the value of Debentures bought.

The 41 year lease, which Bishop had just taken out for himself was valued at the quite ridiculous sum of £19,500. The company was to pay him entirely in script, £16,500 in shares. £3,000 in debentures.

The customary 'expert' reports were issued. All three appear to have ignored the small riverside site at 127260 and it is unlikely that the company ever worked there.

Tom Nicholas of Vagur and Elwyn Valley (an employee of Bishop!) described the property as being on two veins, one green one blue, extending ½ mile along river bank and to the top of a 600' hill with room for tipping and for machinery. He said that it had been working for a year on 2 galleries, but he estimated that when 7 galleries were open 18,000 slates could be made per day to sell at £5 per 1000. He calculated a revenue of £25,000 p.a. with costs of £8,000. Carriage was then costing 5/ (25p) per ton but it was suggested that when the branch railway was built to Llanycefn, transport costs would be 'trifling'. Nicholas' remarks were echoed in further reports by J.R. Price of West Gilfach and W. Pritchard of Rosebush. All three reports following suspiciously closely in content and style, the original press announcement.

Some shares were taken up and there were meetings of already disgruntled shareholders in the September and October. It was explained that of the 45 men at work only 6 were making slates. Figures were bandied about promising big returns within weeks, but it was admitted that there was no immediate prospect of reaching the more profitable Green slate. More fundamental was the problem of transport. The old track through Llwyn yr Ebol farm seems to have been impassable and provision had been made for access from the valley floor which the grand scheme of working from below would require.

Further subscriptions were still being sought a year and more later, despite the debenture interest being already in arrears. Development did progress, the existing working was deepened into a pit, with a tunnel intended to drain and to take block to a proposed mill at the valley floor, but output was minimal. In August 1879 a press report said that 'A new start has been made to develop the trade of the quarry. A good part of heaviest work has been done and a good depth of grey-green slate rock proved'. There was a further and final stoppage before the end of that year, which in August 1880 was explained as being, 'In order that the quarry might be opened out for systematic working on a large scale'. This assertion was backed by the claim that, 'One tunnel 50 yards long and another of 110 yards has been driven and two galleries opened out'.

The company was compulsorily wound up by High Court Order in 1881, by which time Bishop had managed to unload most of his holding. Optimistically Bishop immediately registered a new £30,000 company, but unsurprisingly it failed to attract backers. Some intermittent working was subsequently done, possibly up to the 1930s.

Remains At 129262, quarry area with deep pit. Tunnel (one of two?) open. The building with a possible dressing shed attached and the fine embanked abutment for a rubbish run, predate the Cleddau Company. At 127260 two adjacent faces near river. Small two roomed building, part possibly a smithy. Much waste in the river. Access tracks to both sites are much overgrown.

LLYN SN112272
Unsuccessful trial probably by Campbell of Tyrch in the 1930s.
Remains Trifling excavation & spoil.

NOBLE COURT SN106265
Hillside working, nothing known. Disused by the late 19th century.
Remains Overgrown, obviously long abandoned, some walling. Further similar quarry at 107264 which may have been worked in conjunction although land ownership differs. Other small investigative diggings at 108264. Opposite where the track up valley joins the road are traces of a small trial.

PENCRAIG SN119264

Tiny digging. Local use only? This may be the Parc quarry, (as distinct from the Lily Parc) which was included in a sale of a farm in 1849 which was then let to a Mrs Maria Thomas and sublet to a Mr Phillips.

Remains Excavation.

TEILO VALE SN108268

Hillside working, possibly long disused when it was revived as the Teilo Vale Green Slate Quarries Co. by Davies and Williams of Pontypridd in 1912. They employed about 12 men under the management of John Nicholas, son of Tom, who had managed Dandderwen and Vagur. Besides the Sea Green, Randoms, Rustic Randoms, Peggies and Rustic Peggies, they offered the same four varieties in Olive Green. Most were Sea Green Randoms described as 8" – 22" long and of proportionate width, under ¼" thick, @ 55/ (£2.75) per ton, as well as 'Peggies'.

By the next year employment had risen to 17 and they were hiring a horse full time at a cost including handler, of 3/- (15p) per day. Curiously the horse was owned by a Mr Melchior, the same name as an earlier operator at Llandeilo. An outside carter was employed @ 3/6 (17.5p) per ton. This fixed rate suggests a regular journey, presumably to Maenclochog station via Llandilo Isaf.

By 1914 employment was down to 14, and output varied from 6,000 to 22,000 per 4 weeks say 7 – 25 tons, so with Nicholas' wages being 5/- (25p) per day, the men on a flat rate of 3/- (15p) to 4/- (20p), profits must have been elusive.

They operated in conjunction with Klondike sharing the same sales agent, E. Matthews. Closed at the outbreak of WW1. Some very small scale working during the inter-war years.

Remains Quarrying faces, possible building traces and of the track on which ran their solitary tram.

TEMPLE DRUID SNO98272

It is possible that this quarry served as a vernacular source for Bwlch y Clawdd farm, material from the quarry being used when the farm was rebuilt as a small but elegant mansion in the 18th century. The name Temple Druid house was adopted as there was a Cromlech nearby, allegedly a druid altar. Curiously, as soon as the name was used, the Cromlech was destroyed.

Some commercial quarrying was done in the late 1860s by a William Owen but it was probably only being worked part-time by John Vaughan in 1874 when this advertisement appeared in the local press:

TEMPLE DRUID QUARRIES
'The Proprietor is now prepared to supply parties with Flags, Windowsills, Mantelpieces and Slates of all sizes not to be equalled for size or quality. The fact of the Temple Druid Slate and Slab being in use on buildings in the neighbourhood for more than 120 years and are still perfect is a sufficient proof of their durability. As there is such great demand at present, purchasers are respectfully solicited to send their orders in due time to save inconveniency (sic).

All orders to be sent to the manager Mr John Nicholas, Temple Druid, near Maenclochog.

A few weeks later the quarry was offered for sale. The Particulars stated that there were 'Several veins of slate, one part developed' and that 'The proprietor is prepared to guarantee that the materials will pay 30% at the least for working'.

A 'report' on the 50 acre site was issued allegedly written by Thomas Williams who had been manager at Porthgain until its then recent closure.

It referred to the use of the quarry's material two centuries earlier for building the house and the presence in the neighbourhood of slabs and windowsills up to 8' long from when it was more recently 'Temporally (sic) worked'. It stated that the slab was good for carving purposes and that it would 'bear the high degree of heat of enamelling'.

Emphasising the adequacy of the fish ponds for water supply, it recommended the erection of a 'powerful water wheel to drive 6 saws and 2 planing machines enabling 100 tons to be turned out each month comprising 1100 yards of slab @ 3/- (15p) per yard and 400' of sill @ 9/- (45p) per foot, selling at £180 costing 40% of this to produce'. This figure, it was suggested, could be repeated on several galleries. In addition working backwards and downwards towards the river would open up a 'very superior vein of Green Slates' and there was 'another vein of Blue Slates on the property higher up the valley'. The Narberth Road and Maenclochog Railway, then under construction would 'develop the resources of the property'. Quaintly the report closed inviting inspection, with a warning of 'Trumped up reports of quarries utterly worthless', undertaking to 'Defray the expense of any person who might come if this report is not founded on facts'.

The advert, the Particulars and the Williams report appear to have been composed by the same person!

Advertisements both for the quarry and its products continued in identical grammatical style at intervals for at least the next four years. After that there were occasional announcements for 'Slates of all sizes', but no advertisements for the quarry itself. A sale for £4,000 was nearly made to W.F. Grier of Aberdare in 1884, but it fell through as it was obvious that lack of water would call for steam power and Vaughan backed off from his offer to guarantee profits. Unsuccessful efforts to sell the quarry continued up to 1889.

It probably was idle from then until 1919 when it was re-opened by D.J. Truscott, who was also involved at Glogue. The next year he set up the Temple Druid Slate Quarries Co., predicting sales of 60 tons per week and an annual net profit of £1,400. Even though the post-WW1 slate boom was at its height, subscriptions totalled less than £4,000, so clearly he did not get his asking price for the lease of £5,000 cash plus a like amount in shares.

In 1922 the company was offering, 'Roofing Slates, Olive Green, Rustic & Plain'. However since there is no sign that the alleged 'Green Slate' vein was ever opened up, and the quarry was reported as having been 'stopped' in November 1921, it is likely that they were merely merchanting bought-in material. The company was wound up in 1931.

Remains Quarry faces from which there has been little extraction and vestiges of a small building. There are traces of what could have been a leat leading to this building. Tucker found circular-sawn ends, but these have not been located.

The early 20th century steel waterwheel 3m dia (Thomas Cardigan) with step up gearing of 32-1, drove a generator to light Temple Druid house.

The small excavation at 099267 may possibly have been connected with this quarry.

TYRCH *(Twrch, Turke)* SN145294 & 156291

It is probable that the Foel Dyrch quarry leased in 1780 by William Marsden of Llanglydwen at a royalty of 6d (2½p) on each 1000 slates or flags raised was the Lower site (145294). The earliest record of the Upper site, a little pit high on open hillside, is that it and possibly also the tiny trial at 152297 were being worked by Thomas Griffith in 1798.

The history of both the Upper and the Lower is obscure until the 1860s, when both were being worked by the Turke Quarries Slate & Slab Co, in which John Davies had an interest. The manager was James Charles and it was probably they who first installed water-wheel powered sawing at the Lower site, taking over an ancient flour mill. Local legend has it that over one hundred men were employed, but this is highly unlikely. Although the press reported in 1864 the customary 'extraordinary demand', the company was wound up in 1868, but John Davies still had a hand in things in the 1870s.

Succumbing to the late 1870s slump, both sites became idle. They were bought by John Muscott of Dandderwen around 1890 who seems to have let them to a syndicate of 4 workmen Sam Tudor, Thomas Evans, Griffith Evans and Dan Nicholas. In 1895 F.J. Sellick took over, forming, the Tyrch Silver Grey Slate Co in 1899, with G.B. Thomas managing. Up to 30 men were employed, most if not all at the Lower quarry, diverting the road to allow development and re-aligning the river to expand the working area. They closed in 1908 when they were down to 5 men, Thomas having left to manage Cefn at Cilgerran. Alfred Pritchard of Gilfach bought up the unsold stock.

Shortly afterwards H.L. Lewis reopened the Lower quarry as Tyrch Quarry Co., with James Jeffs managing. They offered Enamelled Slate which they presumably bought in. They closed about 2 years later.

Peter Forbes Campbell (later M.C. J.P.), a native of Manchester moved to the area to take up potato farming. Having married into the much slate-involved Muscott family, he re-opened the quarry in 1921 trading as P.F. Campbell. He re-equipped the Lower quarry where up to 40 men were employed and used the Upper as an occasional source of rock. The water powered mill was abandoned, the 16.5 hp Lunedale turbine by Gilkes of Kendall operating at 233 rpm on a 13' head, which Sellick had installed, was used to drive a generator. The two saws were powered by an 8 hp Diesel engine in a new brick structure. A 50hp oil engine drove a compressor. As the lower working had deepened below the level of the access tunnel through the road embankment, presumably pumping was required, details of this have not been ascertained. He vigorously marketed the 'Silver Grey' slate from the Lower quarry as a premium product, as well as some 'Green', 'Rustic' and slab from the Upper. Like his main competitor Gilfach, he was selling 'Randoms' in mixed sizes grouped according to maxima and minima, which in 1923 were listed at prices ranging from £9 down to £2 per ton, but unlike Gilfach, his main trade was in Sized slates. For these he asked, for example, £42 per 1200 for 24 x 12s down to £4 for 10 x 6s. Although their thickness of ¼" corresponded with second or third grade north Wales slates, Tyrch's prices were up to 15% more than north Wales Bests. Unusually for the time a pre-holing service was offered, charged at from 10/ (50p) to 12/6 (65p) per ton. Also listed was Crazy Paving, 2" thick @ £1 and 1½" @ £1 and 1½' @ £1.5.0 (£1.25) per ton.

By 1924 total output settled down to a fairly steady annual tonnage of just under 400 which was maintained through the late 1920s and early 1930s, but by the mid 1930s output was down to little more than 200 tons, not enough to cover the payroll of almost 20.

All sales were now in lotted mixed sizes, marketed as 'Tyrch Slates', graded according to thickness, 'Bests' being ¼", 'Seconds' 3/8" and 'Thirds' ½", and as well as 'Silver Grey', 'Mottled Grey' 'Green' and 'Rustic' were offered. In 1936, prices for these ranged from £9.10.0 (£9.50) per ton down to £4.10.0 (£4.50). The next year they were advertising prices in terms of area covered at 3" lap, which ranged from 7/- (35p) to 9/- (45p) per square yard, competitive with Lake District offerings, slightly dearer than sized slates from north Wales but much dearer than imports.

Like much Gilfach product, 'Tyrch Slates' had the top corners cropped in Lakeland style, which slightly reduced weight and could give a larger yield from a block.

Crazy Paving was still listed either in 1-1½" or 1½-2" thickness, all priced at 10/- (50p) per ton. Marketing literature showed eminent architects such as Sir Reginald Bloomfield and Sir Charles Gilbert Scott as specifying Tyrch slate for numerous public buildings, schools, churches etc.

throughout Britain.

In 1938 sagging sales had a big boost when the order was obtained for the roofing of the new County Hall at Carmarthen, which with its large, steeply pitched roof accounted for much of the 300 ton output for the year. It is possible that concentration on this important contract caused them to neglect their routine customers, as shortly after its completion lack of orders forced closure.

Remains At the early trial, excavation only. The Upper site is a narrow pit with a collapsed access tunnel and vestiges of 2 dressing sheds.

At the Lower site, the flooded pit is to the east of the road. On the extensive working area to the west, a leat leads to the much degraded original mill building with a water channel below and another alongside. There is a dwelling which probably predates quarry working and a small office built of sawn block. There is a small, part-brick building with lean-to each side, which housed the Campbell machinery. The tunnel through from the working is blocked.

There is a tiny trial at 145289 about which nothing is known, but may have been associated with Tyrch.

Area 5 The Taf Valley

In the upper valley of the river Taf, particularly on the eastern side, are several slate occurrences. Had the vein been more consistent and the quality slightly better, the ease of hillside working and the availability of water would have enabled exploitation to have been more extensive.

Only one quarry of note, Glogue, was developed, and aided by continuity of local ownership, operated almost continuously and usually profitably for some 250 years.

For most of its life product was carted for shipment, usually at St Clears, then an important port and shipbuilding centre. From the late 1870s, the Whitland and Tâf Vale Railway (later the Whitland and Cardigan) eliminated transport problems. For the next 50 years it was able to load product into standard gauge wagons on site.

Penlan and Pencelli were also rail connected but poorness of rock precluded success.

SN177290	Garnwen
186254	Tre Hir
192278	Pencelli (R)
192359	Castellan
197334	Troed y Rhiw *
202333	Pencware
207284	Penlan (R)
211328	Nant y Geifr
220328	Glogue ** (R)
223327	Cwmgigfran
226326	Cwmllwyd
230324	Spite *

CASTELLAN SN192359
Very small, nothing known.
Remains Excavation, latterly a source of rough stone.

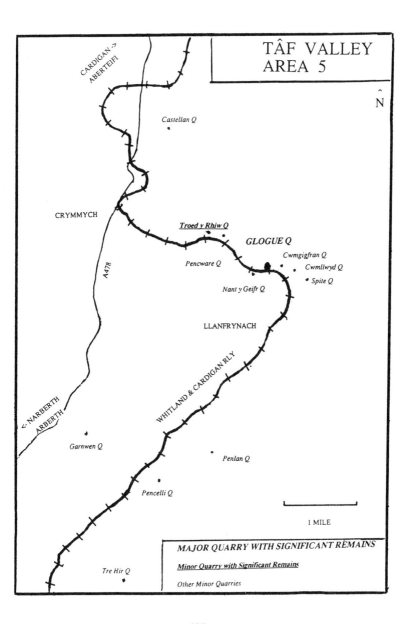

TÂF VALLEY
AREA 5

N

CARDIGAN →
ABERTEIFI

Castellan Q

CRYMMYCH

A478

Troed y Rhiw Q

GLOGUE Q

Cwmgigfran Q

Pencware Q

Cwmllwyd Q

Spite Q

Nant y Geifr Q

LLANFRYNACH

WHITLAND & CARDIGAN RLY

←NARBERTH
ARBERTH

Garnwen Q

Penlan Q

Pencelli Q

1 MILE

Tre Hir Q

MAJOR QUARRY WITH SIGNIFICANT REMAINS

Minor Quarry with Significant Remains

Other Minor Quarries

135

CWMGIGFRAN (*South Glogue*) SN223327

A moderate sized quarry, contiguous with but entirely separate from Glogue. It was said to have been working for 50 years when the ubiquitous John Davies formed the Imperial Slate Quarries Co. in 1866. He had obtained a 21 year leases on land which besides this quarry, also included Cwmllwyd (Clara) and Spite (Lilac) quarries. No rent was payable, just a royalty of 1/20th ad valorem on roofing slate and 1/- (5p) per ton on slab. Having expressed his willingness to sell this lease to the company for £17,000, half in cash half in shares, he and of course Ledgard set about obtaining backing. Investors included Ralph Coulthard of Gateshead, Edward Cooke and John Downes, both of London, the latter grandly styled a Colonial Merchant. In spite of having already embroiled Thomas Key of London, in such doubtful enterprises as Lily Quarries Slate & Slab Co. and Rosebush Slate Co., he too was induced to subscribe. A dividend of 5% was guaranteed for the first year, 7.5% for the second. No guarantee was given for the third year but this was 'expected to be at least 30%'.

These assertions were backed by the usual glowing reports from three 'Independent experts' who unsurprisingly were all employees of Davies/Ledgard companies.

James Charles manager, of West Gilfach (Cnwc y Derin) & Lily claimed that a quarry (unspecified) on similar rock had 'shown a 50% profit for 50 years'. He stated that Cwmgigfran could make slab up to 12' x 9', which could be shipped either at St Clears or Cardigan. Alternatively, product could be put on rail at Narberth Road, saying that the prevailing carriage of 7/- (35p) per ton 'would be eliminated when the extension to the Tenby & Whitland Railway (Whitland & Cardigan Rly. surely?) passed through the property'. He also said that Cwmgigfran had 3 veins 80 yards wide and had been 'much opened up' producing roofing slates as well as slab, 'with tramways and a planer'. No saws were mentioned nor was the power source specified.

Charles went on to say that £4,000 would enable output to be trebled but it would be 'better if a further £1,500 – £2,000 were spent on tunnels and roofing up'. Asserting that this was the 'largest mass of slate in the Principality', he suggested opening two new quarries, presumably between Cwmgigfran and Cwmllwyd and between Spite and Cwmllwyd respectively, inferring that all should be worked as one unit, an ambitious scheme indeed.

Tom Nicholas of Dandderwen broadly concurred, suggesting tunnels and the working on 4 levels, adding that, 'similar slab is sold at Gloucester for £1 per ton more than others in the locality'.

William Pierce of St Brides estimated the vein to be 300 years wide, stressing the need for 'water machinery at the lowest level and the cutting of tunnels'. He said that slab up to 10' x 7' could be made. He agreed that output from Cwmgigfran could be trebled but described the required outlay as 'small'.

These bold ideas, assuming the rock proved suitable, could have resulted in an operation of almost Penrhyn proportions. However the cost would have been enormous and would have called for a rich freeholder, prepared to take a long view on his investment. To have attemped such a thing on a comparatively short lease using capital provided by speculators who had been promised large and immediate dividends was a total nonsense.

It seems there was no rapid take-up of shares as almost a year later, John Battes, the Stock and Mining Share Broker handling the issue, wrote to the press assuring readers that he 'had established the Bona Fides of the Imperial Slate Quarries and that with an anticipated dividend of 6¼% it is no speculation'.

How much investment they eventually obtained or how much work they did is unclear but the quarry was long disused by 1890.

Remains The quarrying area is now a private garden, with

traces of buildings and machine bases. A modern house is on the working area.

CWMLLWYD (Clara, Park, Llwyn yr Hwrdd) SN226326
Very small, pre 1820s? Disused when taken by Imperial Slate Quarries in 1866 along with Cwmgigfran and Spite. It was described as 'good for slab', but it is improbable that they worked it.
Remains Hillside digging with traces of walling and a dressing shed.

GARNWEN SN177290
Some slate working?
Remains Extensive subsequent stone quarrying work has obliterated any relating to slate.

GLOGUE (Glôg) SN220328
A merging of two adjacent hillside workings Park & Pen Park, whose origins allegedly go back to 1685. (Confusingly the former name was later used for Cwmllwyd quarry). It had the advantage that for much of its long life it was in the hands of one family, the Owens.

Oddly, the little quay at Blackpool rather than the commodious St Clears port seems to have been used for shipment.

Little is known of its history prior to the 1830s-40s when up to 50 men were employed in the two excavations, by then deepening into pits. However T. Macdougall Smith, a London geological consultant, in a report commissioned by John Owen in 1854, stated that only 20 men (paid from 1/8 (8p) to 2/- (10p) per day) were working, producing slates and slabs in the westerly pit. The easterly pit which produced what he called flags, was idle and flooded which might account for the drop in numbers.

The report gave examples of production costs and selling prices per 1000;

Duchesses	24 x 12	£2.2.0	(£2.10)	£6.0.0	
Countesses	20 x 10	£1.10.0	(£1.50)	£4.4.0	(£4.20)
Ladies	16 x 8	18/-	(90p)	£2.2.0	(£2.10)
Randoms (Locals?)		8/-	(40p)	13/-	(65p)

These ex-quarry prices were quite competitive, but as Smith remarked, carriage charges were 6d (2½d) per ton mile, instancing that this added 50% to production costs or 20% to selling prices when slates were delivered to either Cardigan or Carmarthen. However he could not justify the £20,000 cost of laying a tramway to the new South Wales Railway.

His recommendations included the clearing of rubbish from both pits, sinking shafts down 45' below their floors and driving tunnels 6' wide x 7' high to connect them with a tramway along the contour to a mill 100' x 38' with 8 saws and 2 planers driven by underfloor shafting from a 25' x 3'6" water wheel. Water was to be supplied by a leat from Cwm Rhosddu. Curiously the plan annexed shows a smaller mill containing only 4 saws and 2 planers. His estimate of a 3000 ton p.a. capability was probably realistic. The mill appears to have been in use by 1860 with just the 4 saws and 2 planers, driven by an 18hp water turbine. Smith's tunnels recommendation had not yet been adopted, material still being brought down to mill level by the old balanced incline sited between the two pits. That year they were advertising:

GLOGUE SLATE QUARRIES
A constant supply of very durable slate is now kept at Narberth road station: also paving flags which by the aid of superior machinery are nicely sawed and planed and arranged into courses ready for flooring. For prices and particulars apply to Mr John Evans, Builder and Contractor, agent for the quarry at Narberth Road Station.

In 1864 and 1865 a full range of slates were being offered

including Duchesses @ £7.10.0 (£7.50) per 1000 at quarry, or £8.8.0 (£8.40) on truck at Narberth Road station or £8.15.0 (£8.75) on barge at Blackpool. The prices for Ladies being respectively £2.5.0 (£2.25), £2.15.0 (£2.75) & £3.0.0. Prices for Locals were 18/- (90p), £1.6.0 (£1.30) & £1.8.0 (£1.40). The substantial advance on the figures cited by Smith reflect the increase of prices that had occurred in the intervening decade. These prices also indicate how carriage costs inflated the price of lower grades relatively more than the better slates.

Planed slate flooring was being offered @ 3½d (1.46p), 4¼d (1.77p) & 4½d (1.88p), per sq/ft.

A variety of finished slab products were also being offered, including Coffins @ 25/- (£1.25), 28/- (£1.40) & 30/- (£1.50).

In 1866 John Owen, shortly before his death, let the property to his son John Owen junior for 60 years at an annual rent of £150, the workforce which had been around 20/30 for some years having built up to about 60. John Jr. clearly had ambitions as he immediately tried to interest a W.J. White of London in forming a company.

White commissioned a report from Robert Hughes manager of Aberllefenni quarry near Corris in November 1867. It is an example of how a normally honest expert might stretch the truth when making such an appraisal. Having realistically described the 278 acre, 1600 yard long property as having the vein running right through it to a depth of 500' and as being worked for 800-900 yards to a depth of 200', Hughes let himself go; 'it is worth of remark that I have never witnessed Slate Metal work so well – the metal can justly rank as one of the best in the country'. He might have truthfully said that about his own quarry, but hardly about Glogue. He averred that productivity was then running at the improbably high figure of 46 tons per man year and that given enough capital, 400 men working on 6 galleries could achieve an even greater per-capita figure. He described the rock as 'inexhaustible'. Hughes' estimate of 20/- (£1) per ton cost of production sounds low even ignoring repairs and renewals, let alone his claim that 'when a more perfect system at the Rock is arrived at ought to be reduced by 2/- (10p) to 3/- (15p) per ton'. His suggestion that revenue averaged 45/- (£2.25) per ton was certainly optimistic.

He did express slight reservations about the split for roofing slate making but his praise of the potential for slab was unbridled. His only criticism was the 7/8 (38p) per ton cartage over bad roads to the railway. It is interesting that Hughes included in his commendation of Glogue the fact that 'like all good slate rocks the dip is 70° towards the south'. This was the case at his own quarry, but it was not necessarily a recommendation. [1]

It may be that White considered Hughes' report too fulsome as in January 1868 he commissioned another from Owen Parry Agent for Dinorwig quarry.

Parry remarked on its 'limited scale', his quarry being 40-50 times larger! He was reticent about rock quality, merely remarking on its suitability for slab. He mentioned the then proposed Railway, suggesting that if a company was formed it should support the Railway. He concluded cautiously, saying that – 'if a moderate capital can be judiciously expended upon the property it would soon give good returns to its proprietors'.

We do not know if Parry's somewhat muted praise

---

[1] A southward Dip suited the northerly working at Glogue. George Owen in 1603 in fact commended some Pembrokeshire quarries as they could be worked in this way, putting it, '– then shall you find the whole quarry loose before you'. Ideal is a northern dip if it can be worked southwards as this avoids the rock being sun-dried and so more difficult to split. As important as the dip is the way the cleavage presents itself, which was not always favourable at Glogue. Because of this, in its last days rockmen complained of working 'Croes y Grein' (across the grain).

turned White off but nothing came of the company proposal and in 1869 Owen was in negotiation with brokers, Cope. Rose & Pearson to raise money on mortgage. They commissioned a new report from T.M. Smith who confirmed that both pits were now open and 'would be capable ultimately of producing 18,000-20,000 tons p.a.'. This wild prediction undoubtedly reflected the extreme optimism of the times. He said little about the roofing slate potential, concentrating on the quality of slab. He concluded by saying that with the 'early prospect of a Railway being made from the Whitland station on the South Wales Railway to the quarry (for which an Act of Parliament has been obtained)', he valued the lessee's interest at the astonishingly precise figure of £39,881.

Owen apparently did obtain some kind of loan, abandoned ideas of selling out and in spite of his background as a draper, proved an able operator.

He backed the Whitland & Taf Vale Railway and in 1873 with its opening imminent, tonnages exceeding 2,000 p.a. and manning near 80, an attempt was made to float the Glogue Quarry Slate & Slab Co. The subscribers to this £100,000 company were W.H. Yelverton of Whitland Abbey and E.M. Godwin of Ferryside, C.K. Anderson, J.S. Anderson, R.R. Brownring, N.J. Senior & R. Paye all from London. A new 100 year lease at £100 p.a. rent with no royalties, was offered.

Robert Hughes', Owen Parry's and T.M. Smith's reports were dusted off and cited and a fresh report from John Muscott of Dandderwen obtained. In his best 'Reportspeak' Muscott described Glogue as 'A mass of rock, especially suitable for making slabs of any size and of very superior quality with only a moderate amount of debris'. He said that the quantity 'may be very considerably increased at any time'. He said that the roofing slate capability was limited but that the potential for slab 'owing to the durability of the material is very good'. He praised the machinery and concluded:

'The Glogue stands alone as a large Flag-producing quarry in South Wales. Taking this into consideration – with the quality of its material – the economy of raising it – the facilities for converting it by means of an ample supply of water-power – and afterwards the connection of the Quarries with the Market. I feel fully justified in saying that, in its present state, it is a most valuable property; and any capital laid out on its further development would no doubt give a large return.'

The floatation was unsuccessful but with the slate boom at its height, trade was good. They were sending fireplaces and Billiards tables to France, such products being claimed to be costing 30/- (£1.50) per ton to produce and selling at 55/- (£2.75). Paving was reported as costing 1/10 (9p) per yard to produce and selling at 3/ (15p).

In 1875 they were apparently contemplating new machinery as they wrote to Pen yr Orsedd quarry at Nantlle seeking information on saws, possibly their unusual De Winton hydraulic feed type. However by the end of the year Owen, possibly anticipating the collapse of demand which did occur a year or so later, was trying to sell out.

His brief description of his property exceeded even the most exaggerated of commissioned reports;

'The quarries occupy the position of Lord Penryn's (sic) in North Wales. Only the 'Glogue' has complete monopoly in South Wales, there being no other quarries in the south worth talking about.'

There were no takers and by 1878 they were selling off rails and offering 3 dressing machines to Sealyham for £18, and in 1880 the Mining Journal was reporting with more accuracy of fact than grammar, 'Not such active work as it was'.

In the late 1870s, they had reviewed the effect having their own railway siding, reached by a new incline, which had obviated the carriage costs to Narbeth Road. The findings were disappointing. In 1874 prior to the railway's opening, their tonnage had been just under 2000 tons, but the average from 1875-1877 was only 2,300 tons. This together with the falling slate market caused Owen to seek diversification.

Every ton of slate and slab produced, created 24 tons of debris which might be profitably made into bricks. It was calculated that if they had 2 single and 2 double Mathews patent brick machines, each capable of moulding 8 & 12 bricks per minute respectively they could, with the necessary kilns, produce 140,000 bricks per week. Moving the debris would cost £500 p.a. 29 extra men would be needed at wages varying from 12/- (60p) per week for 'a lad' to 25/- (£1.25) for a skilled man, averaging 16/- (80p). A suitable manager would want £3. An engine to drive the machines would consume 6 tons of coal per week @ 14/6 (72.5p) per ton. The kilns would need 70 tons, but would accept a lower grade @ 12/6 (62.5p). Oil would cost 8/- (40p) per week and the oddly exact figure of £4.2.0 (£4.10) per week was allowed for depreciation. It was, with some optimism calculated that all this would result in an annual net profit of £14,000.

Samples were made up and sent to relevant engineers who unanimously praised their suitability for engineering purposes. A company, the Glogue Brick and Tile, was mooted but with slate prices low and the quarry down to 30 men, it was thought that a company independent of the slate side would be more appropriate. In 1883 an attempt was made to float the Glogue Metalline Brick but this was not successful.

Shortly before his death in 1886, by which time both pits had tunnel access with terrace working in the west pit and the railway extension to Cardigan was open, Owen again tried to sell. The whole property of 409 acres was offered at £100,000. This was shortly halved and in the end an auction was announced.

The Particulars mentioned the manager's dwelling,

cottages, slate sheds and yards and the 100' x 38' mill with 'machines and turbine', which was said to have, 'Never failing water power'. It was said that the slate was suitable for 'Tanks, Enamelled work, Paving and numerous other purposes besides roofing slates'. It stressed that 'It has been ascertained that the Debris makes some of the finest Metalline bricks & tiles in the world, suitable for sewers, bridgeworks and ornamentation. When this is brought into utilisation, which may be done for a small outlay, the works must prove to be one of the most valuable in Wales'.

An undated abridgement, (omitting the less fulsome parts), of the Robert Hughes', report of almost 20 years before, was used to support the offering.

It appears to have been purchased by Owen's nephew prior to the sale, for an unknown sum. In 1890 he failed to attract backers for the Glogue Brick and Slate Works Co. In 1895 with trade picking up he succeeded, obtaining £6,000 of London based subscriptions, the company paying him this same figure in shares for the quarry.

At about this time a second tunnel was made into the westerly pit where working was by now below the level of the original tunnel. The tramway through this new tunnel joined the lower incline part way down and had a rake of dressing sheds alongside. This and the absence of any easy way to uphaul to mill level suggests that only roofing slate was being made from the western pit. They were selling Locals at 25/- (£1.25) per 1000 but what other roofing slate business they were doing is unknown.

By 1902 with manning down to about 15, they were trying to unload surplus stock, e.g. sawn flags at 1/9 (8.8p) per square yard, and within three years the company failed.

Some local men took over in 1906 trading as The Glogue Quarries Syndicate led by Griffith Thomas and John Rees, with Lloyd Humphreys (a north Walian, probably a member of the family who still quarry at Nantlle), as manager, employing up to 20 men. They succumbed to the difficult trading conditions at the outbreak of WW1 but Thomas continued in business as a slate merchant, retaining the Glogue Quarries Syndicate name.

John Rees having died in 1919, his interest passed to W.J. Williams who in 1920, with G.L. Thomas, granted rights to Londoners D.J. Truscott, F.G. Dawson, J.E. Phillips and A.E. Long. All other than Long who was an engineer described themselves as merchants. They formed the £40,000 Glogue Slate Quarries Ltd engaging Thomas as manager. In soliciting subscriptions it was predicted that sales would immediately reach 600 tons per month, 150 tons of which would fetch £11 per ton, 200 tons £9, and 250 tons £6. The average cost of production being calculated at £5 per ton. It was estimated that within a year output would reach 1500 tons per month and that productivity would exceed 50 tons per man/year. In the heady post-war era the flotation succeeded and almost 19,000 of the £1 shares were taken up.

The over 40 shareholders included farmers, shopkeepers, ministers of religion, steel & copper workers, colliers, housewives and a lady typist (an employee of Long?).

More than £4,000 was spent on development and nearly £3,000 on machinery. Electricity generated by a Blackstone oil engine powered the 4 saws and 2 planers, the turbine being used to grind waste for the revived brick making. Air was provided by a portable compressor, ten unpowered dressing machines were brought into use and in 1921 right on the brink of the collapse of the post-war boom production commenced with 80 men.

In 1923 in spite of disappointing trade, the freehold of the 73 acre quarry and the mineral rights on the surrounding land were purchased for £19,000, part in cash part in shares, a goodly proportion of which apparently found its way into Truscott's pocket.

In 1924 all the directors were voted out and replaced by, H. Johns an insurance inspector from Cardiff, his uncle D.

Williams of Loughor a steelworks manager and H.D. Jonas a London Estate agent. Truscott was 'persuaded' to disgorge most of the shares he had received in part payment for the quarry, it being asserted that he had made 'an undue profit' and Thomas was replaced as manager by J. Humphreys (a relative of L. Humphreys?).

Sir Hugh Thomas of Neyland and Sir Charles Ruthen a Swansea architect were brought in to strengthen the board but Sir Charles having received a government appointment, had to resign almost immediately. His place was taken by E. Harris a Swansea solicitor, who also advanced the company a much needed £7,000 on mortgage.

In spite of the new blood things went from bad to worse. In 1925 a mere 1800 tons of slate was sold, mainly unprofitable rough block. The combination of the tapering off of the post-war building boom and the weight of the product making carriage excessive, killed off brick making.

Closure came early in 1926, leaving Harris as mortgagee in possession, and as guarantor having to pay off the £7,500 bank overdraft as well as settling debts. Though the other directors reimbursed him pro-rata, it was probably only Harris' sub-mortgage on the property which enabled him to do so.

In 1932 Harris' sub-mortgage was called in, the property was placed in trust to secure the interests of the other parties, the company remaining in receivership with the trifling sums of rent for Mill Cottage (adjacent to the mill) and for fields, largely swallowed by the Receivers fees.

During the war the efforts of the Ministry to seize the plant for scrap were resisted as it was felt that after the war rebuilding would create a demand for slate. Indeed a firm did seek an option to restart brick making. Eventually some equipment was sold to other quarries and when after the war, no slate boom materialised, the whole site was cleared of such scrap that remained unpilfered.

The local Council wanted to use the pits to dump old

cars, but had no money to buy it and no waste disposal firm seemed interested.

Everything was wound up in 1970 when Mansel Davies Ltd, who unlike some other contractors had been paying rent for the tip material which they took for hard-core, bought the whole property and after 34 years the heirs of the directors got some of their disbursements back.

Remains The eastern working is now partly filled by tipping but the western, deepest working is undisturbed. However extensive hard core extraction has much degraded the rest of the site.

There are the merest vestiges of the upper incline and of its drumhouse which lowered material to the working level in pre-tunnel days. No trace has been found of the lower incline from the mill to the railway siding. The mill foundations and leat are hopelessly overgrown. Of the tunnels, only the inner end of the upper west pit one is identifiable. The site is now in reuse as a transport depot. The railway siding is partly traceable, but nothing remains of the internal tramways, which it is believed were of 2' 4" Gauge as opposed to the near universal 2'.

The powder house ½ mile to the north has not been identified.

NANT Y GEIFR SN211328

A very small quarry yielding a coarse, irony slate, possibly only used as a source for farm materials. Listed as active 1866.

Remains Quarrying face.

PENCELLI SN192278

Hillside/pit which W. Bishop, who was also involved in the Cleddau Valley Company, developed in 1877 to take advantage of the partly opened Whitland & Cardigan railway. In 1879 a press report said that, 'the rock becomes harder to the South West with a tunnel to tap the lowest floor steadily advancing'. A further item the next year said, 'a good railway siding has been put into the works and prepared to send off slate'. The incline was described as 'the best constructed in Wales', and 'with the lower tunnel having entered slate rock, will in a few months be well equipped for work'.

The piece which appeared in 1881 merely reported, 'Good sales to London'. All three undoubtedly originated from Bishop himself and presaged his formation in 1882 of the Elwyn Valley Slate & Slab Co. to take over this quarry and Penlan, both of which were proving duds.

In spite of the recession, Home Counties investors stumped up enough of the £25,000 authorised capital to pay Bishop £5,500 in cash (and the same amount in shares), for the two quarries. An aura of respectability was given by appointing as Visiting Superintendent, D.C. Davies, who had just published his authoritative work, 'Slate and Slate Quarrying'.

The schedule buildings and equipment they took over at the quarries included; 'A 210 yard incline with drum, wire rope, a double line of rails, rollers, points, crossings &c. A large planing machine with knives, a sawing machine with saws. A machine for hoisting stones. A Blacksmith's shop with anvil &c, a Carpenter's shop, Slate making and dressing sheds. 35 tons of tram rails, for use of tramway, 3 trams, 3 wheelbarrows, 12 pickaxes, 6 shovels, 6 mattocks, 4 jumpers, 4 scrapers, 2 ramming bars, 1 calybar (?), 3 bars, 2 travails, (stools with a fixed blade for trimming slates), 3 sledges, 3 hammers, 2 rock chisels, 12 splitting chisels, 6 mallets, 2 reeces, (i.e. Rhys, the massive Oak mallet used for breaking block).

The tramway rails and some of the equipment were at Penlan, but the 'sawing machine' and 'planing machine' are puzzling as there is no mention of anywhere to house them or power them, nor has any evidence been found of their location at either quarry.

Any success was short lived as in 1885 the railway company was seeking to lift the by then disused siding.

Remains Much spoil, tunnel access (blocked) to overgrown pit. The tramway formation passes under the railway to the site of the siding and the possible location of machinery. Vestiges of incline, but buildings which were on the upper level have not been located. Upstream, a pond may have been intended as a reservoir.

PENCWARE SN202333
May have been tiny slate digging.
Remains Filled in.

PENLAN (Elwyn Valley) SN207284
A hillside quarry worked by William Bishop with Thomas Nicholas as manager. It was described in the press in May 1878 as, 'having been opened by Mr Bishop some time back', who was 'in the process of constructing a ¾ mile, railway'. The next year it was reported that 'the rock improves with depth and good slates and slabs are being made'. In 1880 the press reported that it had been 'connected to the Whitland & Cardigan Railway by a short railway', adding that the property was 'awaiting a new owner', so possibly it was idle and for sale.

Obviously no sale was made, as it formed, with Pencelli part of Bishop's 1882 Elwyn Valley company. By 1886 the railway siding had been lifted.

The tramway was relaid and a temporary incline installed during WW1 to facilitate the removal of timber.

Remains Thickly overgrown. Working face and vestige of one small building. The ¾ mile 2' 6"? gauge tramway to the railway siding near Rhydowen is partly traceable, the dwellings where it crossed the public road may have had quarry associations.

SPITE (Lilac, Nant y Weirglodd) SN230324

Small hillside pit. It was out of use when it was taken by the Imperial Slate Quarries Co. in 1866. Its rock was described as 'the finest' of the three quarries of the group. Although they were advised that it would take only 'a few hundred pounds' to put the quarry in order, it is doubtful if they ever seriously worked it. Abandoned before 1890.

Remains A shallow working with cutting access. A wall with storage niches was clearly intended for 3 or 4 dressing sheds, but only one seems to have been built.

TRE HIR SN186254

There was a press report in August 1879 that 'Lead had been found at Tre Hir slate quarry, worked by Mr William Bishop' (of Pencelli & Penlan). This presumably planted item may have referred to this tiny vernacular working.

Remains Filled in pit.

TROED Y RHIW SN197334

Moderate sized hillside quarry, presumed late 19th century but nothing known. Although the railway passed close by, it was not used, presumably because the small output did not justify the cost of bridging the river to reach it. Some restricted working in the 1920s, possibly with some kind of portable sawing machine.

Remains Quarry face with cutting access, sizeable dressing/stocking area developed on spoil, revetted by slate walls. Slight vestige of a dressing shed. A few hand sawn ends, but among newest waste some very neatly circular sawn ends. The only possible sign of machinery is a precisely cut 30" x 25" x 4" thick slab with housings cut in each edge and having two, ½" diameter bolts at 6¾" centres. There is a finely engineered access track and much use of rough slab for walling in the vicinity.

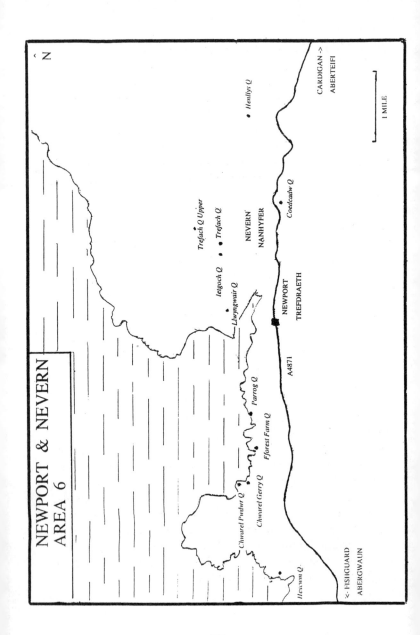

Area 6 The North Coast

These tiny quarries probably represent the origin of Slate working in the region, certainly they are some of the earliest for which we have written reference. Near Newport are the sea cliff workings referred to by George Owen at the beginning of the 17th century as being the source of 'Tiling Stones'. Others near Nevern, are those which Owen wrote of as producing 'Russet stone – dug very large'.

Very much maritime, they were centred on the ports of Newport, Nevern and Cwm yr Eglwys (Dinas harbour).

Records are sparse, remains scanty and undoubtedly there were other sites, particularly among the ephemeral cliff workings of which all trace has been lost. This sea-cliff working probably extended north of Cardigan. In fact Lochtyn quarry SN312544 near Llangranog may have produced a slate of sorts.

SN997389	Hescwm
019399	Chwarel Pwdr
020397	Chwarel Gerry
026394	Fforest Farm
034396	Parrog
071402	Llwyngwair
081404	Ietgoch
084404	Trefach *
086410	Trefach Upper
094387	Coedcadw
113395	Henllys

CHWAREL GERRY SN020397
Tiny clifftop working. This, or Chwarel Pwdwr may be the Craig y Dyffryn where a Mr Harries was making Locals in the 1870s.
Remains Excavation.

CHWAREL PWDR SN019399

Tiny clifftop working.
Remains Excavation. Much evidence of boat-accessed working on the nearby cliffs and beach.

COEDCADW SN094387

Site listed by Owen in 1603 as producing 'The finest stones'.
Remains Overgrown shallow pit.

FFOREST FARM SN026394

Tiny workings in gorge. Material possibly sent out over the beach. In December 1845 it was advertised that, 'All those capital Slate quarries now in work on the farm at Fforest in the Parish of Newport', would be let. Attempts were made in 1875 by about a dozen London men to float a £50,000 company, the Dinas Slate & Slab Co. It is not known if this was a genuine attempt to cash in on the high prices and slate shortages of the time, or whether it was fraudulent. In any event it did not succeed.
Remains Scarring of faces. Much slate on beach.

HENLLYS SN113395

Slate working listed 1603. Probably this was quarry named in 1866 as 'Sir Thomas Lloyd's Quarry'.
Remains Series of very shallow pits, that have nothing to positively identify them as slate workings.

HESCWM SM997389

Clifftop quarry, possibly evolved out of a maritime working. D.R. Reynolds and John Rowlands were here in the 1860s & 1870s respectively and it may have been they who did most of the work now to be seen. The Hescwm Slate & Slab company was formed in 1878 with a capital of £30,000, by a group from the Home Counties with the averred intention of working slate here and in the neighbourhood. In spite of steeply falling prices and demand they did raise some money and the company was registered. It was dissolved in 1887, probably without any digging having been done. An attempt was made at revival in 1931, an anecdotal account saying that 'The slates were so poor the company went out of business'.

Remains Several small faces near the cliff top, possible signs of working lower down cliff.

IETGOCH SN081404
Tiny open working.

Remains Trace at roadside.

LLWYNGWAIR SN071402
Small and probably ancient working, providing slate for estate use.

Remains Working face, waste heaps. At the mansion are some fine slabs including some serving as outdoor tables, which probably came from Cilgerran.

PARROG SN034396
One of several cliffside workings to the west of Treffraeth (Newport) estuary such as the ephemeral Traeth Samwl, Chwarel Ffeiraden and Aberstep, which worked from the 17th century to the late 19th century. Some were only accessible by boat, others being accessible by cart at low tide. Trans-shipment was made at Parrog, the harbour for Newport.

Remains Scarring of cliff faces and at the harbour, wharves and buildings.

TREFACH (Lower Mill) SN084404
Rather larger than others in the locality. In 1869 an attempt was made to raise capital to develop it, probably by John Davies.

J.R. Price who was running Llandeilo quarry, William Pritchard the manager of Rosebush and a Mr Samuel

Jenkins F.G.S. were persuaded to 'concur in expressing favourable opinions as to its prospects'. Price is alleged to have believed that 'the slate vein might be worked to a very great profit and be in all probability a safe object of capital investment'. Pritchard was more cautious but did suggest that 'The property deserves to be tested so as to make it worthy of the attention of the public'. Jenkins was more definite stating that 'it is of very great prospective value and presents a good field for the introduction of capital'.

These three might have concurred, but no one else did, and the project fell through. When the land was advertised in 1874, the quarry appears to have been let to Stephen James at a rent of £13.10.0 (£13.50) p.a., unusually the dressing sheds and plant apparently were the landlord's property as the purchaser was required to buy them at valuation. It was again advertised in the same terms in July 1878.

Remains Curious curved wall and a building (36' x 10') with two doors may have been used for reduction. No evidence of sawing. Access track past old mill, (not used for slate purposes?) but adjacent buildings now in re-use may have been associated with quarrying.

TREFACH UPPER SN086410

A tiny hillside working, mentioned in 1874 Sale Particulars in conjunction with Trefach, but probably only produced for local use.

Remains A small excavation much overgrown.

Area 7 Cardigan & Teifi

From at least the 18th century slate 'Stones' figured prominently among cargoes shipped at Cardigan. This trade was boosted in 1785 when Parrog slate merchants, Thomas & John Davies bought a large granary at Cei Teifi, (now the Cardigan Heritage Centre). This enterprise became the Cardigan Mercantile Co. encompassing Sail & Rope making, Ship owning, Coal & Timber merchanting etc., but its success remained slate-based, mainly on the transhipment of slate paddled down the Teifi in lighters from quarries at Cilgerran and Fforest. All of which contributed substantially to Cardigan's growth as a port and shipbuilding centre. By 1833 Lewis' Topographical Directory was saying of Cardigan, 'Exports, Butter and Oak Bark, but the staple article is slate'.

Ironically, these quarries which brought prosperity to the port, also hastened its decline. Their dumping of waste in the Teifi apart from restricting river navigation, robbed the estuary of vital scour, causing silting up of the port. [1]

There were two substantial groups of quarries, Fforest and Cilgerran, both on the lower Teifi, the latter being collectively as large and interesting as any in south west Wales.

For much of the 19th century Cilgerran was an anachronistic hotchpotch of little independent diggings. Yet well before the end of the century, at least three had become important mechanised operations, which because of the impracticality of using the river for power, made extensive use of steam. Latterly using the Whitland & Cardigan Railway, they outlasted most other quarries of the region.

All the rest were small mainly serving local needs. Besides those listed, there were other diggings such as the little roadside site, Penllech yr Ast SN219483 at Penparc, which may have yielded a rough slate. There were also several, deeper into south Cardiganshire, such as the tiny

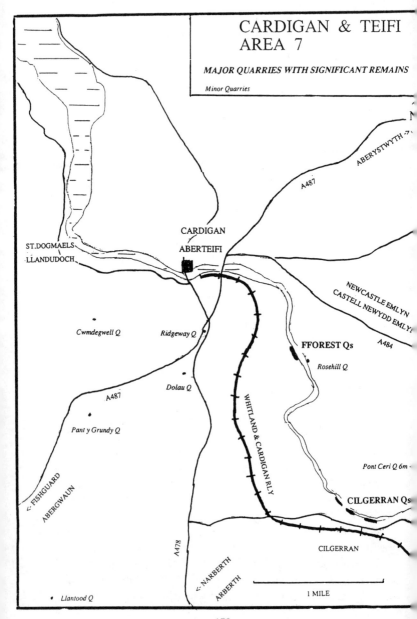

CARDIGAN & TEIFI
AREA 7

MAJOR QUARRIES WITH SIGNIFICANT REMAINS

Minor Quarries

ABERYSTWYTH

A487

ST.DOGMAELS
LLANDUDOCH

CARDIGAN
ABERTEIFI

NEWCASTLE EMLYN
CASTELL NEWYDD EMLYN

A484

Cwmdegwell Q

Ridgeway Q

FFOREST Qs

Rosehill Q

A487

Dolau Q

WHITLAND & CARDIGAN RLY

Pant y Grundy Q

Pont Ceri Q 6m

FISHGUARD
ABERGWAUN

CILGERRAN Qs

A478

NARBERTH
ARBERTH

CILGERRAN

1 MILE

Llantood Q

158

Blaenrhiwfallen SN559599 at Talsarn or the larger Penpwll SN419410 at Llandyssul, which also were said to have produced rough slate.

SN158419 Llantood *
163442 Pant y Grundy
163454 Cwmdegwell
178446 Dolau
180452 Ridgeway
190450 Fforest * *
192448 Rosehill
195431 Cilgerran * *
296419 Pont Ceri
505511 Llechwedderi (Unmapped)
585487 Cwmrhys (Unmapped)

CWMRHYS SN585487
Moderate size, supplied building block for the Peterwell Estate, with the likelihood of some roofing slate output. Two men employed 1906.
Remains Overgrown tip, excavation filled as rubbish dump.

CILGERRAN TOWN QUARRIES SN195431 etc.
The town and castle of Cilgerran perch precariously above the almost 200' deep Cilgerran gorge, as if guarding their ancient port and borough rights. Reputedly these rights allowed any 'Burgess of Kilgerran' to 'dig for stones' without charge, a fee being payable to the Portreeve only on any which left the town. Since the cliffs of the gorge consisted substantially of high quality slate and were readily accessible from the river towpath, they provided a handy source of slate for local use.

From Cwm Plysgog, immediately west of the castle, for almost a mile upstream, outcrops occur in three distinct exposures. Thus the workings can be classed as:

CASTLE QUARRIES	SN195431
MIDDLE QUARRIES	SN198429 – 200428
UPPER QUARRIES	SN203428 – 209430

Eventually three dominant quarries would emerge, Dolbadau SN198429, Plain 204428 & Cefn 205429, significantly the only ones to have working space at river level and to be able to obtain cliff-top ground.

When real commercial exploitation commenced in the early 19th century, it was by small partnerships, who may have employed men made idle by the closure of the Tinplate works at Llechryd.

When Fenton, writing in 1810, referred to quarries at Cilgerran, there were at least three; John & Moses Griffiths, digging at the base of the castle, brothers George & David John working immediately below them and John Bowen at Cnwcau at the western end of the Upper outcrop.

By 1830 Thomas Morgan and John Griffiths were also working, probably in the middle area and like Bowen and Moses Griffiths, were now calling themselves Slate Merchants, although their trade was described as being of a 'Trifling and piddling nature'.

By 1840, the Portreeve was making formal lettings of numbered plots with 80-100 yard frontages onto the river bank. Some plot holders worked part-time, combining quarrying with other occupations such as farming or coracle fishing, giving rise to the sour observation that 'With one exception the quarry owners are men of little substance'. That exception was probably the emerging Stephens family.

Lessees were required to pay at Court Leet, 3d (1.3p) for every 1000 slates sent out of the town and 1/6 (7½p) for every lighter of flags sent down river, but the four 'Overseers of Stones' who acted for the town Bailiffs rarely enforced collections. Nor, presumably because it was realised that operators had little alternative, was resolute action taken against dumping waste in the river. The fine imposed on James Stephens in 1841 being just 1/- (5p).

In 1850 Moses Griffiths having retired, his part of Castle was run by his son of the same name, but the Johns' patch had been taken by James Stephens, trading as Stephens & Sons. Their operations being valued p.a. at 12/6 (62.5p) and £2.10.0 (£2.50) respectively.

There were now seven workings at the Upper Quarries; Plain valued at £8, which was John Bowen's old Cnwcau patch, where his son had gone into partnership with William Stephens. It was now held by James Stephens who in 1847, had also rented some land further up river beyond the town boundary, where there was space to work and to erect buildings on the river bank.

The smaller operators, with their valuations were: William Evans, £2.10.0 (£2.50), Lewis & Thomas John. £5.5.0 (£5.25), Thomas Morgan, £6.12.6 (£6.62), Evan Bowen & John Bowen Jr., £1 and Griffith Evans £1.10.0 (£1.50). James Matthews who had been an earlier digger having apparently dropped out.

By 1860 there were at least a dozen separate partnerships and the numbers engaged in quarrying were increasing. The 1851 census had shown 47 quarrymen in the parish, the 1861, 63. These may well have been underestimates since it was claimed c1860 that the three or four 10 ton barges in use were making 12 journeys per month. This total of at least 4320 tons p.a. would have called for well over 100 men. This discrepancy could be partly accounted for by some workers being from other parishes. The output and manning figure is supported by an assertion made at the time that the failure of the Council, (who had succeeded the Bailiffs) to collect tolls, involved a loss of revenue of some £70 p.a. Incidentally, operators were also now supposed to pay annual rents of 5/- 10/ (25p-50p), but it was said that even these were not paid because, 'The owners are unprincipled and dishonest'(!)

By this time the ultimate pattern of ownership was starting to appear.

The Castle Quarries were still in the same two hands. In 1866 James Stephens was for a third time prosecuted by Mrs Gower of Castell Malgwyn for blocking the river with his waste, but although the depth of water at his quarry had allegedly been reduced from 10' to 18", local opinion was that his Castle quarry was 'the least offender', action only being taken against Stephens because he was in the largest way of business.

The remainder of Castle, now known as Chwarel Moses, was still held by Moses Griffiths junior, now joined by his young cousin, yet another Moses Griffiths. Later they took on Stephens plot and trading as Bwmdwll Quarry continued to work unmechanised on a reasonable scale until the end of the century.

The Middle Quarries were now coming into the picture. Dolbadau (Chwarel Griffiths) was small and still called Chwarel Bach but was being expanded by James & John Griffiths, taking advantage of the extra room which their site alongside the Town Dock gave them. Eventually they would have 3 lighters of their own, Mouse, Lion & Ocean. Next to it Chwarel Pwdwr was held by Ben Daniels & David Griffiths, and alongside it a tiny working Bensha, occupied by William Mathias and Owen Davies, who was described as a farmer and stone mason.

Of the Upper Quarries, Plain, by far the largest was in the hands of Jeremiah Stephens and his son of the same name, trading as Stephens & Co. Having a stretch of dead rock to the west they were able to have a proper tipping area, served by a tramway. Their works at Mwldan, Cardigan (later the Cardigan Engineering & Foundry), enabling them to be the only proprietors able to offer machine-sawn and planed slab.

Just upstream was a tiny working leased by William Thomas who had just taken it over from William Francis. He does not seem to have had much luck as he gave up a few years later.

Beyond, were a further 5 workings, from west to east these were leased respectively by Lewis John & Arthur Mathias, (afterwards Owen Davies & William Mathias?). John Bowen, (later Bowen & Jones). John Morgan & James Stephens (Heddwch Quarry?). John Evans & Bowen (Ianto Quarry) which was later run by Evans' sons William & James. The endmost of these 6 diggings (Klondyke or Ucha) was still worked by Stephens & Sons. The marginal profitability of the smaller workings is shown by the frequency with which they changed hands.

The 1871 census shows the number of quarrymen had dropped to 49 and certainly the number of lettings had fallen. Up river as far as and including Plain there had been little change. East of Plain, Thomas John & John Lewis, John Harries and David Michael were digging but at least three of the plots were vacant or idle. It was clear that even in the then booming market, very small scale quarrying could not be successful, particularly at the eastern end where the rock did not favour roofing-slate making.

Capt. Erasmus Gower JP. of Castle Malgwyn must have already recognised that amalgamation and adequate capital were required and saw opportunities for himself. In fact the owners of Tyddynshiefre quarry near Fairbourne had already done so, and in 1865 had sent their manager, Meredith Jones, to report on east Cilgerran. When they decided not to take any action, Gower bought the report the following year.

Jones said that the railway would 'soon be finished' (it would be, in 20 years!), 'eliminating' the 1/ (5p) per ton lighterage to Cardigan. He suggested that the 160' high face be worked in four galleries. Since the rock yielded good slab, a steam engine should be set up 'in the field at the top of the quarry' where block could be sawn and planed and waste dumped. The slab was predicted to sell for 40/ - 80/- (£2 - £4) per ton.

Gower then obtained his own report by John Paull of the Llangollen Slate & Slab Co. who suggested that a steam engine be sited at the side of the quarry with a tunnel southward to dispose of rubbish (?). Gower, having his own Cefn y Garth land at the top of the quarry, seems to have been taken by the Jones report as he asked him to cost his suggestions. They were: £1,650 per gallery, engines, saws, planers incline and carriages £3,500, trams and sleepers £800, clearing rubbish and forming a roadway £900, smithy and carpenter's shop £200. This outlay of £12,000 being expected to produce a profit of £4,000 p.a.

Gower obtained yet another report from D. Pritchard of Penrhyn Quarry, Bethesda, undated but presumably from the early 1870s. In it the cost of slab making per ton by machinery was analysed as 'Quarrying 4/- (20p) Sawing and planing 9/- (45p) Clearing rubbish &c 3/- (15p). Coals, cartage, management & incidentals 3/-'. Machinery would cost £2,000-£3,000 and that during its installation, productions should be 'allowed to stand' (i.e. suspended). Pritchard said that the 'Top rock should be worked back for 50ft-60ft for the whole width and working it to a depth of 130ft'. In this latter he broadly concurred with Jones in that the face should be advanced rather than deepening the existing pits.

In 1874 Gower took over the vacant patches, some land along the river which had been separately rented by Stephens and of course his own tract at the top. He named the whole Cefn quarry, trading as E. Gower & Co. with one of the Dolbadau Griffiths' managing it.

He immediately set about implementing the Jones/Pritchard proposals, putting in a steam mill with 2 saws and a planer, a tipping ground alongside it and an incline to haul up to it. Whilst this was going on he sold, mainly from stock, such things as Local slates at £1 per 1000, Pig Troughs at 1/4 (6.7p) per foot and Milk Pans at prices varying from 1/3 (6.2p) - 1/8 (8.3p) per gallon capacity. Surviving accounts suggest that his sales the first year were about £300, doubling and redoubling as the mill came on stream. He also seems to have been stuck with a goodly amount of unplaned slabs from the pre-mill operations, as he was advertising in 1879:

Slate Flags
A large quantity of rough unplaned Flags are making for sale from 1½" - 3" thick and from 4' - 10' long at prices varying from 6d - 1/- (2½p - 5p) per square yard at the quarries. For prices and particulars apply Mr J.T. Griffiths of Dolbadau, Cilgerran. Manager Cefn Quarries.

In spite of the asking prices being only about 10% of the going rate for planed material, these continued to be advertised for many years, 'at greatly reduced prices for cash'.

Advertising also started in 1879 for planed slab and other mill products saying that they were, 'to be sold at Engine Shed at Cefn Mawr at the top of the hill' emphasising that buyers could collect 'with no hill for carts to ascend'. It was also advertised that, 'Mr E. Gower's Stones can also be obtained at Mr Gower's quay at Cardigan on application to Mr Evan Tucker'.

The prices were: slab, planed both sides 6d (5p) per sq/ft for 1" thick to 16d (6.7p) for 4" thick. Windowsills 8d (3.3p) per foot run for 2" thick to 16d for 4". Milk Pans 1/3 (6.2p) per gallon and Pig Troughs 2/ (10p), with small surcharges for Lighterage to Cardigan. Locals @ £1 per 1000 were the only slates listed and since no Lighterage charges were quoted for them, they were presumably only being sold at the quarry.

In 1894 with all-rail dispatch well established obviating the lowering of product from the mill to the river, Gower formed the Cefn Quarries Syndicate. Besides recycling the Jones and Paull reports of thirty years before, an 1890 appraisal from Pritchard was cited. This referred to the 'abundance of the rock' and it being – 'Exceptionally free from waste, indeed much more so than the majority of Slate

Quarries that have secured a high reputation'. Pritchard also mentioned 'ampleness' of the tipping ground and commended the 'advantageousness of the production of large slabs', adding that, 'There seems to be an increasing demand for slabs, especially of large sizes'.

It was claimed that sales over the last three years had averaged 900 tons giving a return of 18% but that this tonnage 'could be trebled and within two years could reach 5,000, bringing large dividends'.

Shares were taken by A.M. Harries, W.H. Marsden, F. Wright and his cousin F.L. Gower, all English industrialists, and by C.M. Richards of Cardigan. Capt. Gower's contribution was the quarry itself, for which he was issued £10,000 in shares and debentures, half the authorised capital.

The Gower land on which was the mill etc, was leased at £100 merging with a 2½% royalty on sales, plus £100 per acre on any additional land they might need. The quarry itself remained on a let of £5 p.a. from the Town Trust which had succeed the old Corporation in 1890.

A 120 hp gas engine to power a compressor for drills was put in and for a time things went well but before the end of the decade, output was plummeting. A bonus system was in operation which in effect gave the men an extra £1 for each £2.25 of additional saleable material they made, but offered no incentive to clear the rock falls and rubbish which were obstructing the best faces.

Extra men were taken on to attempt to clear the top gallery and the steam crane was swapped around to clear the pits, but the block which No. 3 pit yielded was unsatisfactory. In any case all three Penllyn pits, particularly the pumped pit, No. 1 which also drained pits 2 & 3, were getting too deep to be safe. When in 1899, Pritchard was again brought in to advise, he was against further work in the pits and suggested that provided they did not have to 'rely on reports of elderly workmen that good rock did lie under the 15' of loose rubbish', a new pit be opened at the quarry top with a new incline powered by the existing haulage engine.

John Jenkins who had been brought in from Meirionnydd to replace Morris Davies as manager, was against the quarry top pit idea, suggesting chambering underground near river level. In the end neither proposal was adopted and work continued on the galleries. Further dispute arose about the installation of additional saws and planers and the use of a channelling machine. (To facilitate extraction of block from the faces.)

The slab trade had held up better than the roofing slate trade during the 1880s and by the late 1890s was good but with the new century came a slackening of demand, bringing problems to Cefn which were not solved by replacing John Jenkins by Griffith Bowen Thomas who had been managing Tyrch.

The Syndicate fell into receivership in 1906, the schedule of plant included 2 Hoisting Drums with Wire Ropes, 2 Semi-portable Engines, 1 Vertical Engine, 1 Steam Derrick, 3 Saw benches, 3 Planers. This schedule is clearly incomplete. The gas engine and compressor does not appear, nor does a lathe to turn the pillars and balustrades, which were being made at Cefn in the early 1900s. Although Hoisting Drums and Engines appear there is no mention of the Blondin which was almost certainly in service by this time. This type of overhead ropeway, unknown in the slate industry outside Caernarfonshire, allowed material to be picked up from both the pits and terraces.

G.B. Thomas was appointed receiver and he continued to run a part of the quarry, Capt. Gower allowing him use of machinery on which he had apparently retained title. It all ended in tears with Gower implying that Thomas was failing to pursue the best interests of creditors and Thomas accusing Gower of frustrating his efforts to do so.

In 1909 under pressure from Gower, Thomas with David

Davies, a Cardigan solicitor, formed Kilgerran Quarries Ltd, taking over the mill etc. on Gower land on a 20 year lease at £20 p.a. merging to a 2½% royalty plus £60 p.a. per acre for additional land. They resumed extraction from the part of Cefn they defined as 'lying between Morgans quarry on the east and Stephens (i.e. Plain) to the west'. Using the name Pats Quarry, they continued to produce slab, including billiard tables, also making mock stone blocks from slate powder.

Following financial trouble in 1912, Thomas and Davies resigned and R. Hoare (of the banking family) took over putting in £5,000. The mill was partly re-equipped, a rail link to Cilgerran station was planned but never built.

After wartime closure a restart was made, the lease for the mill and tip land being renewed in 1921 at £40 p.a. merging to a 2½% royalty but before the year was out, work ceased and the plant was sold off.

In the meantime at Plain, the Stephens' had made further progress. By 1890 they were trading as J.W. Stephens Slate & Slab Co. and immediately prior to WW1 were employing 24 men. Slab was sawn and planed in a steam powered mill alongside the road, close to the railway station. Block for the mill was at first hauled up a ramp by means of horses walking along the road, pulling a rope around a pulley. After Pats closed the Blondin was taken over to haul over the abandoned Pats workings. A steam crane was used when the working deepened into a pit, which since the quarry was well above river level, could be drained by tunnels.

Picking up some of the Kilgerran Quarries customers prolonged their survival, but with the slab market declining at an even faster rate than the roofing slate market, closure came in 1924.

Of the Middle Quarries, little is known of Chwarel Pwdwr. In 1895 Daniels and Griffiths were still there and alongside it, Owen Davies carried on alone, probably part time. Davies later merged the two workings and his son continued to have a man there occasionally up to circa 1930.

On the other hand, Dolbadau prospered under John Griffiths. He built a steam mill with saws and a planer, above the quarry and reasonably close to the station. Block was raised to it by a steam winch fed by the mill boiler. The working also having gone down into a pit, a steam crane was used to lift block out of it and although at first a drain to the river was cut, presumably as the work deepened a pump had to be used.

In the early 1900s Griffiths' son William took over trading as Griffiths & Co, employing 6 men. With some outside finance, he seems to have survived WW1 better than most and was briskly trading during the post-war boom, receiving enquiries from as far afield as Leicester. Having his own kiln, he made a feature of his enamelled products which it was rumoured were produced by his own unique process ,the secret of which he had obtained from an European immigrant.

In 1921 his backers, D. Davies, T. Griffiths, K.O. Larsen & S.M. Larsen, possibly sensing the end of the boom, withdrew their capital, a total of nearly £400. He seems to have had little difficulty in finding other finance from London.

No price lists were published but Griffiths' own note of charges for 1921 survives. He recorded prices in 1000s, varying from £28 for 20 x 12 to £17.5.0 (£17.25) for 16 x 10. He was also now offering Damp Course slates in the more traditional 1200s at prices varying from £15.2.6 (£15.12) for 16 x 9 to £7.5.0 (£5.25) for 12 x 9. All these Free on Rail prices, were about in line with the north Wales lowest grades. For Locals, priced by the 100, he was asking a mere 12/- (60p).

Planed slab was now being offered in the north Wales 'Lot' classifications. The cheapest @ 130/- (6.50) per ton being 2" thick classed as Lot 1 (2'6"-5' long, under 15 sq/ft per piece). The dearest @ 200/- (£10.00), 1" thick Lot 2 (5'-7' long, under 21 sq/ft per piece). These were about 20% below north Wales figures. (Lot 3s [over 7' long or 24 sq/ft per piece] were not offered.) In addition unplaned Flags were offered @ 9d (3.75p) per sq/ft over 3' long and 8d (3.33p) under 3' long, about half north Wales prices.

Even these, for the times moderate, prices did not hold for long. By 1923 Roofing Slates were down by some 30%, (e.g. 20 x 10s, £18), and planed slabs 6' x 2' (thickness unspecified) were being offered at 13/- (65p) each and rough sills for only 1/6 (7½p). One quote for 16 finished sills 4'-5' long, 'Throated & Weathered', totalled only £1.10.9 (£1.54), less than 10p each delivered. A Urinal set comprising; a Back 5'6" x 4'6", two Divisions 4'6" x 1'6" x 1" and a Channel 5'6" x 10" x 2" was quoted delivered to Cardiff for a mere £3.5.7 (£3.28), offering to sand all the faces and edges for an extra 13/ (65p). After deducting carriage of say 50p-60p, this quite complicated half-ton item worked out at little more than half the 1921 price of slab and scarcely covered labour costs.

Griffiths soldiered on through the 1920s, extraction ceasing at the end of the decade. Fortunately many of his account books survive to provide a record of some of the minutiae of the latter days.

The 1929 Day Book shows some roofing slate was being sold into the immediate area. One order was for 20 x 10 @ £16 per 1000, delivered to Boncath. Damp Course slates 12" x 4½" went to Ebbw Vale, carriage paid for £2.9.0 (£2.45) per 1000, (both about equivalent to Blaenau's ex-quarry prices). But most of the rest were 'Locals', both quantities and delivered prices (per 100) being to say the least, modest, e.g. 350 Locals @ 11/ (55p) to Blaenffos, 4000 Locals @ 9/ (45p) to Milford Haven, 2300 Locals @ 9/ (45p) to Haverfordwest and 800 Locals @ 8/9 (44p) to Fishguard. Some ex-quarry prices for Locals were as low as 6/- (30p).

Slab was now being priced by the square foot delivered, about matching the prevailing north Wales ex-quarry 'Common Flagging' tonnage prices, but quantities were not large e.g. 673' slabs at 8d (3.3p) for P.G. Davies Carmarthen did give a total of over £22 but 134'6" of Flags @ 9d (3.75p) per ft were delivered to Cardigan for little more than a fiver.

Finished goods were giving a slightly better return but in very small units of sale e.g. an Enamelled table slab for W. Michael, Cilgerran 8/ (40p). An enamelled chimney piece for £2.10.0 (£2.50) also for Cilgerran. A Chimneypiece, 4'8" x 3'6", Sanded edge & face was £1.15.6 (£1.77) plus 2/6 (12½p) carriage to Boncath. A Cistern (comprising 5 planed and grooved slabs and 2 threaded rods) was delivered to Cardigan for £1.5.0 (£1.25).

A number of 'sculptors' (Monumental masons) were regular customers such as T. Jenkins of Cardigan, Williams of Brynaman, W. Thomas Llandovery and Anthony also of Llandovery who doubled as a Coal Merchant. They took slab and occasionally finished 'Grave Coverings'. One bizarre item was a 'Coffin without bottom' (!) @ £3.7.6 (£3.37p) plus 10/ (50p) carriage to Fynnonbedr.

Much of their output of slab products were invoiced to south Wales merchants such as Geo. H. Cann of Swansea, Perkins, Seward & Richardson of Cardiff or Davies Bros. of Newport, the goods usually being delivered direct to their valleys customers. Some of the orders were reasonably substantial, e.g. 130 boxed enamelled chimney pieces, 8" Jambs 37½" Risers x 36" wide, were £293.10.0 (£293.50) delivered Bargoed. 32 slabs 6' x 2'3" x 1¼ were £63.16.0 (£63.80) Free on Rail. 673' of slab @ 8d (3.3p) to Carmarthen totalled £22.8.8 (£22.43). Most of the large merchants paid monthly but many others took up to six months or more to settle, often making derisory part payments.

Many orders were pathetically small e.g. 3 Slabs 5' x 3' x 1" sent to Swansea for £3.13.6 (£3.62). 2 Slabs 6'6" x 3'6" to

Pontypridd for £3.18.0 (£3.90). 2 Pantry slabs went to J.F. Weaver of Swansea for 17/6 (87.5p) each. Some orders were for single items at £1 or less, including planing, cutting to size and carriage. One transaction was for 18 slates 20 x 10 at 7/6 (37.5p) lump sum. The books show that some of these trifling accounts were never paid. Those that were, usually had the 'odd pence' or even the 'odd shillings' knocked off the payment.

Quotes show various extras e.g. a 7' x 2'2" slab was quoted at 34/- (£1.70) with sanding 6/- (30p) per face and a similar figure for rounding the edges. Enamelling on one face would be charged at 6/-, on both faces 12/6 (62.5p) with an extra 2/6 (12.5p) for carriage on enamelled items (presumably for additional packaging).

Enamelling business was not brisk, as both Black and White ochre in turps were bought by the stone (14lb), turpentine by the single gallon and gold size by the pint.

After extraction ceased, William's son J.T. Griffiths, carried on trading during the 1930s, working off accumulated stock and trying to recover outstanding debts. He was able to clear his remaining 4,500 20 x 10's in one load to Daniels of Boncath, and some Locals sold in lots of several thousand, all at trifling prices. Mr Anthony of Llandovery took respectable quantities of slab @ 7¾d (3.3p) sq/ft, but most transactions were for just a few shillings.

Sales continued on a diminishing scale, mainly to the immediate area, but one order for a single slab came from as far away as North Walsham in Norfolk. His final order in July 1938 was from W.J. Morgan of Cilgerran for a 'Covering' charged at 12/6 (62.5p).

Remains Castle Quarries. The early Chwarel Moses workings between the castle and the river have been largely obscured by later tipping and river reclamation work. The old John's/Stephens' patch later incorporated with it as Bwmdwll which penetrates to the east of the castle is much overgrown but to the front of it are some traces of the rubbish tramways. On the far bank of the river is a small trial of which nothing is known.

Middle Quarries: About 300m upstream, immediately beyond the Heritage Centre and the road which served both the Town Dock and the quarries, is Dolbadau quarry. The quarry faces remain but the pit has been filled. A house, Tŷ Ystrad, where the occupants suffered the noise and dust of the quarrying, almost in their back yard, still stands. Above, in a private garden are buildings including the office (lately re-roofed in Cilgerran slates) and vestiges of the mill. Nearby is the supply pond for the boiler and traces of the uphaulage. The site of the enamelling kiln has not been identified.

Immediately beyond are the faces of Pwdwr and its merged adjoining working, with some traces of walling. There are 3 other minuscule diggings probably abandoned before the mid 19th century.

Upper Quarries: About 300m further up river, the Plain tips commence, with a tramway formation parallel to the towpath. A road curves back rising to town level, up which block was hauled to the mill which is now occupied by Messrs. Reids drapery warehouse. Inside it, a fine wall-crane survives.

In the quarry itself, there was much disturbance, including the cutting of a road and filling of the pit, during the 1960s river clearance. There are vestiges of the arching of two drainage/access tunnels, some lengths of 3" x ½" bar rail and some hand-sawn ends.

Next along the river are the more extensive Pats/Cefn workings. There is one building 20' x 12' which since it has hand sawn ends nearby may have provided shelter for sawyers. A date DW1897 presumably denotes a repair. There is a small unidentified construction on the river bank. Nice slate steps lead up from this point. There is a further small building possibly from the early Stephens & Son era, near it on walling, is a date of 1880. The pits have been filled.

Above, are the terraced workings and the remains of the big tip, now much reduced in height, having been used for road building and from where hard-core and rough slab are still sourced. The Blondin anchor points are visible. The steam mill is incorporated into the buildings of Bryn Siriol farm, the farmhouse itself being partly constructed of Cefn mock stone blocks and nearby the quarry office survives.

CWMDEGWELL SN163454
Tiny diggings on either side of a stream, listed 1603. In 1849 William Davies of Haverfordwest offered for sale.
'An excellent Slate and Slab quarry situated in parish of St Dogmells, (sic) now in full work'.
Remains Traces of Excavation.

DOLAU SN178446
Small hillside quarry.
Remains Slight traces of excavation.

FFOREST SN190450 etc.
A series of hillside workings along the south-west bank of the river Teifi. Being on Forest farm land, that name is sometimes used, but they should not be confused with the small Fforest Farm quarry at SN026394.

On a continuation of the Cilgerran occurrence, but separated from it by a fault displacement, most men and several lessees were from that town. Land access was difficult, hence it was even more river dependent than Cilgerran and several men and their families lived on site.

The various openings were not all simultaneously worked and were at times under separate tenancy. Caution is called for in applying names to them as some, particularly Gigfran (often anglicised as Raven), may have referred to different diggings at different times, hence it is difficult to be sure who worked where.

Apart from some trifling extraction at SN190451, there

were three 'big' quarries now generally identified as:

Carnarvon or Lower	SN190450
Ffynnon	191449
Tommy	191448

and three 'small' quarries:

Bach	192447
Gigfran	193445
Forever	193444

A mention in a lease of 1621 to a quarry on land bordering the Teifi may have referred to slate working here, but the first known operator was Thomas Edwards who rented Forest Farm from landlord John Symmons in 1766. By 1819, Edwards' Slate Merchant grandson John had taken over the digging, his landlord now being Thomas Lloyd of Coedmore whose father had, in 1790, added a tract south of the river to his extensive estate.

In 1827 a new lease was granted to Elinor Edwards, Thomas Edwards' widowed daughter-in-law and her two younger sons, the above mentioned John and Thomas, a Victualler. The limits of this quarrying let approximately conformed to the extent of work seen today, and referred to 'divers openings' made by the Edwards. It contained an undertaking by Thomas Lloyd not to work slate, on either side of the river up as far as Castle Malgwyn and Llechryd Weir. Confusingly it makes an exception of four quarries let to 'certain persons by who the same are now worked', and effectively gave first refusal to the Edwards brothers should any of these four be vacated. Lloyd also reserved for himself the right to open one quarry for his own purposes. Whilst it is made clear that this latter right could only be exercised outside the Edwards' let, it is not obvious if the four existing quarries were on or off the Edwards patch. This remains an enigma, particularly as Rosehill quarry on Coedmore land was then being worked.

A resolute clause was included prohibiting the dumping

of rubbish in the river or on the marsh, although it seems the river had already been diverted by previous tipping.

The Edwards were soon in trouble. In 1834 Thomas, in spite of having borrowed £80 from his brother John, failed to pay his £42 half of the year's rent. John undertook to pay it for him accepting his share of the quarry in settlement. Two years later John found action being taken against him by landlord Lloyd who alleged that for 12 years he had been dumping into the river. With no likelihood of his being able to stump up any damages, Lloyd bought him out for a rather generous £100, waiving £50 arrears of rent. He also bought the tools and equipment for £60 and the horse for £8.

Thus equipped Thomas Lloyd assisted by his brother Oliver, ran things himself, trading as Coedmore Slate & Flag Quarries. He appointed a Thomas Davis (Davies?) to act both as foreman and selling agent. Unusually, the disposal of rubbish was contracted out to a William Ladd, not on a tonnage basis but on daily rates. Around 4-5 men were employed by Ladd, who charged Lloyd 1/2d (6p) per day for filling drams and 2/6 (12.5p) for a Haulier and horse, also occasionally a boy at 6d for 'driving the drams'. It is not clear whether Ladd himself was paid or if he took a rake off from these somewhat modest wages. Also unclear is the payment for 'nights'. A typical week's bill would be for 5 or 6 days and up to 4 nights, the same 1/2d being paid for both days and nights. It would seem that a full night shift was being worked by the Rubblers even in winter, which suggests that Ladd was, with the Lloyd's knowledge, dumping in the river under cover of darkness!

David Phillips, a Cilgerran blacksmith was paid a retainer of £15 p.a. to repair drams, wheelbarrows, boat chains etc., making quarterly claims for materials, e.g. 2½d (1p) per lb. for Iron, 4d (1.6p) for Steel and for 'Russia Iron'.

He was paid 2d (.8p) per shoe for farrier work, 1/6d (7.5p) for making 'Scalping Knives' (Slate trimming knives?), a few pence each for items such as chisels, wedges and plugs, and

1d (.4p) for sharpening them. These latter payments are unusual as quarrymen themselves normally paid for the supply and maintenance of small tools. The Lloyds settled Phillips' accounts promptly but were in the habit of 'knocking off the odd', e.g for an account of £6.6.10 (£6.34), Phillips received just the bare £6.

Some of the output was sold locally but most went to places such as Swansea and Carmarthen and quite a substantial proportion to Waterford, shipped on Lloyd's smack, 'Ruby' which traded there from Cardigan and Milford.

Not that output was vast, from December 1839 to April 1840 140,500 slates were sold (300-400 tons p.a.). Of these less than 9% were sold locally, yet provided almost 15% of the estimated total profit of £28, reflecting the growth of competition in more distant markets.

The extent of the Lloyds workings is unknown. They certainly were at Carnarvon or Lower Quarry, which had been opened by the Edwards and there is an 1840 reference to him having 4,500 slates at Bach worth 9/ (45p) per 1000. He also made a loan in 1838 to William Ladd to 'open up Raven', i.e. Gigfran.

As landlords, the Lloyds must have enviously watched their tenants' lighters' going down river with loads for eager buyers. As operators themselves they discovered that those buyers were more eager to take slate than to pay for it. Also the Irish economy was going into decline not only robbing them of a major market but also bringing some substantial bad debts. By 1843 with over £300 on their sales ledger, they ceased trading and set about trying to recover the numerous outstanding accounts some of which were for as little as 1/6 (15p).

What happened next is obscure. William Mathias was granted a lease in 1860 at £50 p.a. from T.E. Lloyd MP. (His father Thomas Lloyd having died in 1859), but this appears to have been a re-lease of ground previously worked by

James Mathias.

In 1868 there was a lease to James & William Stephens of Cilgerran trading as Stephens & Sons at a rent of £40 which probably included the largest working, Tommy, which James Stephens may have been working earlier.

It is thought that it was the Stephens who installed the mill with water-turbine driven saw(s) and a planer and they may have built additional cottages, as well as rebuilding the wharf. They had three or four 10 ton lighters, said to making a total of 20 voyages to Cardigan per month. If true this indicates an output of 2,400 tons p.a, a surprisingly high figure.

In 1876 it is not clear if either Stephens or Mathias were still in the picture, but a Sambrook & Davies partnership were, as there is a record of them selling slate to the Coedmore estate. The next year, David Sambrook & David Owens were renting at £70 p.a. and in 1878 were granted a lease at £60 p.a. on 'Lower Quarry' (Carnarvon) and Gigfran and it is inferred that no one else was digging at this time.

The 25 year lease was a complex document, including the usual unenforceable ban on dumping waste in the river. It recognised that the tenants had repaired a stable and other buildings and that they would be constructing a wharf at Rosehill and repairing a road from it to the Cardigan-Llechryd road. This would enable them to boat across the river and cart to Cardigan. The right to use Forest farm roads was also included, suggesting that dumping was already interfering with navigation to Cardigan.

Lighters were of course still in use, it being stipulated that one was to be made available to the Lloyds six times per year to transport 'Sand, coals, slate slabs, pipe, manure or any other material from Cardigan to Pwllnewydd under Coedmore'. The lease gave the Lloyds the right to buy slate at 5% discount in addition to a 5% off for cash settlement and allowed Sambrook & Owens the use of the 'railway' (presumably the tramway along the river bank from

Tommy) and the 'planing machine'. Oddly, there was no mention of saws.

The rent was to be restored to £70 when the Whitland Railway extension was completed, which at the time was considered to be imminent. (It did not come about until 1885 and of course, never served these quarries.)

Sambrook & Owens repeatedly advertised in fulsome terms:

Re Opening of Forest Quarries

Messrs. Sambrook & Owens beg respectfully to announce that they have reopened the above quarries so celebrated for the excellent quality of its Slabs and Slates, which they intend working under their personal supervision trusting by attention to business and moderate charges to merit a share of the patronage of their friends and the public.

Messrs. Sambrook & Owens beg to call special attention to the size of the slabs taken from the Quarry being without joint or blemish of any description and thoroughly suitable for any purpose including that of first class tombstones and cisterns &c.

They also beg to announce that they have had built expressly for them a new and commodious lighter by which all orders entrusted to their care will be forwarded to Cardigan most expeditiously.

In 1880, discouraged by the slump, Sambrook dropped out and Owens continued in a small way.

In 1883, by which time Owens was a year and a half in arrears with his rent, a visitor from Dublin, W.D. Handcock wrote, 'In a dilapidated building the planer and cutting machines were out of order, with the turbine dry through neglect of the water course'. He also observed that 'A few men and boys were working with picks and crowbars and with 'edges' and handsaws split and squared. Further on were some rude dens about 5' high with men preparing slate'. He suggested that by taking water from 'above the rapids, an undershot waterwheel of great power could be used'. He remarked on the rubbish runs as 'long drawn out lines of waste tipped anywhere', and suggested rubbish should be used to form a causeway to Cardigan.

Early in 1885 Owens seems to have been winding down as he obtained permission from T.E. Lloyd to surrender the lease of 2 cottages. Later that year, faced with the prospect of being forced to contribute to a proposed river dredging scheme, he surrendered his quarry lease and departed the scene owing 4½ years rent.

There appear to have been intermittent lettings during the late 1880s and the 1890s at £60 p.a. and finally, in 1897 one to a David Owens (Not the same one?) at £80 p.a.

From then, until the surviving rent rolls cease at Michaelmas 1909, there were no further lets. A photograph taken by Tom Mathias, dated 'c1910' captioned 'Forest Farm Quarry', shows a steam crane hauling out of a small pit. It is possible with some certainty to place this at the extreme northern end of the Carnarvon quarry. Thus it would seem that there was one last attempt to win rock from these, by then substantially worked out diggings.

Reputedly the cottages were occupied until 1927, when their furniture was carried to Cardigan by boat.

Remains The site is now the Welsh Wildlife Centre, reached via the trackbed of the old railway. The quarries never used the railway as its 1885 opening coincided with the cessation of serious working. The original access track was past Forest farmhouse (189439).

Near the now lost site of the mill, Carnarvon cottage has been rebuilt as the 'Coracle Building'. Nearby, Forest cottage has also been repaired, behind which is a limekiln much antedating slate working. Adjacent are the rubbish runs in the marsh and traces of the main wharf.

Along the river are portions of the masonry which formed a wharf and reinforced the old towpath to carry the tramway which connected the three 'big' quarries, Carnarvon, Ffynnon & Tommy, to the mill area. The pit in the former has been filled and all are just overgrown faces, except Tommy which has a 40m cut and cover tunnel giving access through the waste bank. Some hand-sawn ends indicate the production of slab prior to the construction of the mill.

Beyond, the three 'small' quarries, Bach, Gigfran & Forever, are at a higher level with much waste piled in front of them. The abundance of trimmings and lack of sawn-ends suggest that these only produced roofing material.

There is some walling etc., but scarcely a trace of any buildings such as dressing sheds in any of the workings. Along the river bank, some vestiges of the leat which fed the mill turbine may be seen.

A dearth of machine-sawn ends suggests that due to lack of fall the turbine may not have been a success.

LLANTOOD SN158419 & 157418
Tiny workings possibly only for farm use. Listed 1603.
Remains Scratchings in the rock (also at 157418 & 162417).

LLECHWEDDERI SN505511
Extremely small, in occasional use early 1900s. Mainly building block.
Remains Small working area and tip.

PANT Y GRUNDY SN163442
Listed 1603. Nothing else known.
Remains Quarry face. House and transport depot on site.

PONT CERI SN296419
Probably never continuously worked, its quite substantial exposure of readily accessible rock must have made it a useful source for Slaters over a long period. E. Davies worked it on his own on an 'as required' basis 1906-1912 and it

may have been single-man worked post WW1.

Remains Face only. Old dwellings in vicinity are roofed with its material.

RIDGEWAY SN180452

Marked as working on 1888 OS map, at which time it may have been run by E. Gower of Castle Malgwyn.

Remains Part exposed quarry face.

ROSEHILL SN192448

Two small adjacent workings on the north bank of the Teifi, probably mainly for estate use and of which little is known. The Coedmore rent roll for 1819 shows a nil entry against '2 Slate Quarries' but from 1820 until the extant record ends in 1825, J. Evans is shown as paying £8 p.a. under this heading. That this referred to these quarries is supported by a 1819 letter from Thomas Lloyd stating that he was 'considering letting out two quarries on Rosehill farm'.

In 1834 new tenants at Rosehill farm were warned against digging slates from the quarries or opening new ones.

Nothing further is known until 1877, when Sambrook & Owens of Fforest supplied Phillips, the tenant of Rosehill farm, with 3,000 Locals @ 15/- (75p) plus 1/6 (7.5p) Lighterage per 1,000 and also sending 500 slates by cart. It is improbable that these were being delivered to Rosehill and anyway repairs would be paid for by the landlord. Thus it is possible that these were to fill an order on Phillips' behalf and that this Phillips was at least trading in slate, if not actually working this quarry.

Remains Two main and some small working faces, traces of walls and of a wharf.

[1] The river Teifi had been navigable to Llechryd, but when the Penygored tinplate works there closed c1805, there ceased to be an influential river user. Thus when in the early 19th century those quarrying along its banks declared open season on using it as a tip, it fell to landowners and ad-hoc

committees to try to keep the river passable. The quantities tipped were immense, production of say 5,000 tons of saleable product p.a. would generate at least 50,000 tons of waste, most of it ending in the river. It caused the river to alter course at Fforest, and in places reduced its width by three-quarters and its depth by two thirds.

Watch was kept on suspected offenders but piles of spoil seen on the river bank at nightfall would have by 'mysterious forces' vanished by daybreak. Some quarries were made to put rubbish into lighters but this was only dumped downstream. The saga of Admiralty surveys, prosecutions, condemnations, resolutions, stipulations and clearance schemes, only finally ended with the Rivers Authority's dredging scheme in the mid 1960s.

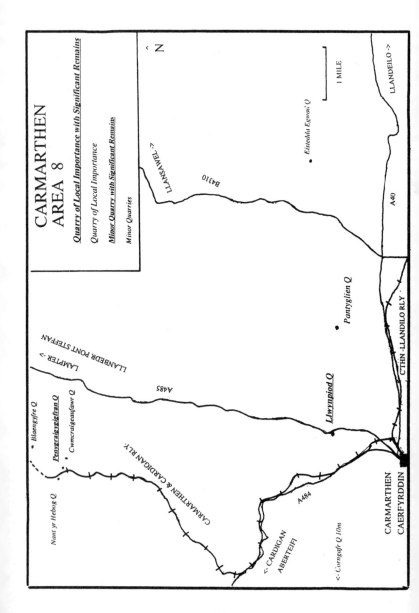

CARMARTHEN
AREA 8

Quarry of Local Importance with Significant Remains

Quarry of Local Importance

Minor Quarry with Significant Remains

Minor Quarries

N

1 MILE

LLANDEILO ->

Eisteddfa Egwad Q

A40

B4310

LLANSAWEL ->

Pantylien Q

CTHN.-LLANDILO RLY.

LAMPTER ->

LLANBEDR PONT STEFFAN

A485

Blaengdyfe Q

Penycraigysteffan Q

Cwmcraigcaufawr Q

Llwynpiod Q

Nant yr Hebog Q

CARMARTHEN & CARDIGAN RLY.

<- CARDIGAN
ABERTEIFI

A484

<- Corrugaf Q 10m

CARMARTHEN
CAERFYRDDIN

Area 8 Carmarthen

Slate quarrying in South West Wales was not confined to the old county of Pembroke and its borders. There were numerous scattered workings in a band along the Tywi valley, which in fact extended at intervals right into central Wales. Almost all were very small, catering solely for local needs.

There were several near Carmarthen, some of which were more substantial and were very much part of the south west Wales quarrying scene.

Llwynpiod had a steam driven mill and Penycraigygigfran shows some attempt at underground working in the Meirionnydd manner, which apart from the putative work at Summerton, is the sole known example in the region.

Some output was shipped and later railed at Carmarthen. It is possible that loadings may also have been made at Abergwili and/or Nantgaredig on the Llandilo-Carmarthen line.

SN266227	Corngafr
418328	Nant yr Hebog
420326	Penygraigygigfran *
425327	Cwmcraigeaufawr
428339	Blaengyfre
433229	Llwynpiod *
465224	Pantyglien
535238	Eistedda Egwad

BLAENGYFRE SN428339
Tiny quarry of convenience.
Remains Excavation

CORNGAFR SN266227
The £20,000 Birmingham based Corngafr & Tredolan Slate Co. was registered in London in 1860 to exploit this tiny

quarry and Tredolan near Solva. Nothing is known of the latter, it has not been located, its probable site having been lost under St Davids airfield. The astonishing sum of £6,000 was paid for the lease (which may have included both properties) but since payment was in shares the figure was academic.

Matthew Francis, the main sponsor, had previously been involved in some dodgy lead mining flotations, nominated his brother Henry as manager here and Griffith Jones at Tredolan.

They do not appear to have ever worked, their sole action appears to have been to seek an 'Expert Report' on Congafr from Jones. Since Jones was a potential employee, this report was even more fulsome than was usual. It contains the customary reference to ease of working and to the quality of the rock, as well as to the proximity of the river Cynin for water power. Reference is made to 'Two north Walians having made some thousands of slates about 60 years previously, with some to be seen on houses in the neighbourhood'.

It is not known if this unsuccessful flotation was a sincere attempt to work these quarries but one must conclude that it was not. There seems to have been some work done in the later 1860s but not by this company, although it was not formally wound up until 1882.

Remains Excavation, nearby farm buildings are of great interest.

CWMCRAIGEAUFAWR SN425327

A tiny quarry of convenience on land taken by Knight and Maunder in the late 1860s, unlike the neighbouring Penygraigygigfran quarry it was not developed.

Remains Lately in use as a source of bulk fill by Cwmgraigeufach farm, now filled in.

EISTEDDA EGWAD SN535238
Hillside quarry, very small yielding marginal material. Operating 1830s? closed well before end of 19th century.
Remains Possible building

LLWYNPIOD SN433229
According to Lewis' Topographical Dictionary of 1833, there were two slate quarries in the parish of Abergwili, 'employing 50 persons and making roofing slate in the locality', presumably referring to Llwyndpiod and Pantyglien. Certainly by this time loadings at Carmarthen Town Quay included roofing slates, although it is only from the 1840s that Llwynpiod is named as a source.

It was advertised for sale in 1848 as being, 'In full work with tramways', but its main development was in 1864 when the Pant y Glien Slate & Slab Co. was formed to operate the two quarries. Although the company only lasted 2 years it spent £3,000 on 'erections' which presumably included the 25' x 40' mill at Llwynpiod, which housed 2 saws and a planer.

William Evans of Glangwili took it on, benefiting from the Pantyglien company's reckless expenditure. The workings went downward forming a pit drained to a stream by a 120m tunnel. The haulage incline was driven from the mill's horizontal steam engine. When the rubbish area to the south of the mill became full, a bridge was built to permit tipping to the east of the road.

In 1883 the Mining Journal mentioned, 'A rather nice green slate quarry near Carmarthen'. (Although it was in fact argillaceous.) By this time there were advertisements for 'Milk Pans, Milk Tables, Steps, Window Sills, Cisterns, Gravestones, Mangers, Plinths, Chimneypieces and Plain and Enamelled Slabs of all descriptions'.

An account dated 1895 shows T & S Evans (Williams's sons?) selling 1" x 2½" Window Sills, five 3'3" long and one 2' long @ 10d (4.2p) per foot, charged at 15/2½ (76p) the lot.

Another is for two 'Hearths', 3' x 1'6" and 2' x 1'6" respectively, plus a 'Doorstone' 3'6" x 1'6" @ 5d (2.1p) per foot totalling 5/8 (28p).

By 1908 Thomas Evans was trading on his own with 8 men. By 1912 his payroll was only 5, mainly producing building block and fines for brick making, which a steam lorry carried to Carmarthen. Closed by 1920.

Remains The pit has been filled, but the rebuilt mill substantially follows the lines of the original structure with boiler house and stack alongside. It is possible to discern the engine platform, the mountings of the overhead gantry, drainage arrangements for the saw cooling water and the run of the haulage rope. Maps confirm that only one door was used. The layout of the mill would have permitted dressing machines but these do not seem to have been installed. this and the absence of trimming waste confirms that latterly at least, few it any roofing slates were made. There is no evidence that the Enamelled Slabs were stoved on site.

The tips, including the one on the far side of the road reached by a bridge (demolished), have been almost completely removed for landfill. All trace has been lost of the drainage tunnel which had a constructional shaft halfway along its length.

Numerous examples of Llwynpiod slab can be seen in Carmarthen, as well as possible examples of coarse roofing slates.

NANT YR HEBOG SN418328

A small hillside working, probably only producing for local use.

Remains There is a small house with an attractive curved garden wall, formerly 'Quarry Cottage' it has been converted to an open ended structure and re-roofed in GCI. A tiny shed (mapped as roofed in 1889) and a curious structure consisting of a tiny stone lined dugout accessed through an equally tiny shed. Just below the site is a more substantial excavation but this was probably a source of fill for the 1860s railway construction.

PANTYGLIEN SN465224

Two small hillside workings, 18th century or earlier. Offered for sale in 1848 as two separate quarries (on either side of the road), plus 8 cottages. The larger, westerly working had been let to Henry Williams in 1846, but at the time of the sale both appear to have been idle.

In 1864 the Pant y Glien Slate & Slab Co was formed to develop here and at Llwynpiod. The easterly working was used for tipping and some downward excavation was done at the western site. In March 1866 a dividend of 18% was paid, in November that year the company was in liquidation.

Early the next year it was offered for sale with a 48 year lease at £200 p.a. plus royalty 1/20th. Structures including houses, being included. Particulars stated that it was old established, that £4,000 had been 'recently' paid for it and £3,000 spent on development. Whilst the particulars seem to refer Pantyglien, the costs must have included Llwynpiod. It is believed that it was taken by William Evans along with Llwynpiod, some limited extraction being done up to the 1900s.

Remains Quarry face with filled pit. Tips on the far side of the road were reached by a level crossing. There is no trace of the two quarry buildings which appear on maps. Housing associated with the quarry is still in occupation. Numerous roofs in the area are of Pantyglien slate, including the Bishop's Palace at Abergwily, (now the Carmarthen Museum).

PENYGRAIGYGIGFRAN SN420326

A working on the easterly flank of the tiny Nant Aeron valley of which remarkably little is known. An unregistered company, the Carmarthen Slate Co was formed in 1861 by some Ffestiniog men. Where or indeed if, they worked has not been ascertained but the tunnelling here makes this site a possibility.

A report in 1867 stated that 'Penygraig' and Cwmgraigeaufawr were being developed by Knight and Maunder, slate merchants of New Inn near Pencader on a 140 acre site of which three-quarters was said to be slate. It claimed that there was 'ample water for a 25' wheel' and that the 'Carmarthen & Cardigan Railway was within 100 yards'. A royalty of one twentieth accrued only on slate which was sold and paid for. The report also said that slate sills and flooring from here had then been in use for 80 years.

Nothing is known of Knight & Maunder's activities, but it was undoubtedly they who built the tramroad formation to the railway, but they cannot have produced any significant output.

The railway had opened from Carmarthen to Llandyssul in 1864. Originally Broad gauge, at the time of the above report the Manchester & Milford Railway was laying a third rail past the site to enable through running to Carmarthen from Pencader junction.

Remains A puzzling site. The hillside quarry deepened into a pit, accessed by a tunnel, is straightforward enough, but the rest is enigmatic.

The most striking feature is a massive causeway across the valley which consumed much of the total waste generated. The primary purpose being to carry a tramway across the valley which made a sharp turn south to run up a railway siding via a nicely revetted formation. The upstream side of the causeway is very deeply silted and the stream by-passes the embankment via an arch only a few feet lower than its top. The 1889 25' map shows the river entering opposite to and at about the same level as it then, as now, emerged. On that map the arch appears to be an adit, with a second one at a lower level, now deeply buried in silt.

Surface water enters the quarry but readily percolates

down what could be a debris-filled roofing shaft. [1] There is also an apparent roofing shaft coming up from below near the access tunnel. These suggest that underground working was at least attempted. No entry for such working except possibly the aforementioned arch, has been found.

The reference to water power in the 1867 report, suggests that the causeway may have also been intended to serve as a dam. If so any machinery would have had to be located at a low level downstream, from where dispatch of finished product by rail would have called for uphaulage.

Other than an embrasure no buildings have been identified. There is a limited amount of roofing slate trimming waste, and some hand-sawn ends from the making of slab. However it is tempting to speculate that a very ambitious operation was planned.

[1] In the Meirionnydd method of underground working, Roofing Shafts were driven upwards along the top of a sloping vein, immediately below the overlying country rock. Extraction was made downwards and sideways to develop a Chamber.

Index

193

207284	Penlan (R)	5
211328	Nant y Geifr	5
220328	Glogue ** (R)	5
223327	Cwmgigfran	5
226326	Cwmllwyd	5
230324	Spite *	5
296419	Pont Ceri	7
266227	Corngafr	8
418328	Nant yr Hebog	8
420326	Penygraigygigfran	8
425327	Cwmgraigeaufawr	8
428339	Blaengyfre	8
433229	Llwynpiod *	8
465224	Pantyglien	8
505511	Llechwedderi	7
535238	Eistedda Egwad	8
585487	Cwmrhys	7

Sources

Abridged Bibliography:

Evans, D. Gareth, *A History of Wales 1815-1906,* (UWP, 1989)

Fenton, R., *A Historical Tour through Pembrokeshire* (reprint) (Dyfed CC, 1994)

Gale, John, *The Maenclochog Railway*, (Milford Haven, 1992)

Jenkins, J.G., *Life & Traditions in Rural Wales*, (Sutton, 1991)

Jermy, R.C., *The Railways of Porthgain & Abereiddi*, (Oakwood, 1986)

Lewis, E.T., *Mynachlog Ddu*, (Cardigan, 1969)

Lewis, W.J., *The Gateway to Wales* (Dyfed C.C. 1990)

Lindsay, J., *A History of the North Wales Slate Industry*, (David & Charles, 1974)

Morris, J.P., *The North Pembrokeshire & Fishguard Railway*, (Oakwood, 1977)

Owen, G., *A Description of Pembrokeshire*, (London, 1603)

Owen, M., *A Memoranda of Col. John Owen*, (Ipswich, 1893)

Page, J.H.R., *Forgotten Railways of South Wales*, (David & Charles, 1979)

Phillips, J.R., *A History of Cilgerran*, (London, 1867)

Price, M.R.C., *The Whitland & Cardigan Railway*, (Oakwood, 1976)

Richards, A.J., *A Gazeteer of the Welsh Slate Industry*, (Gwasg Carreg Gwalch, 1991)

Richards, A.J., *Slate Quarrying in Wales*, (Gwasg Carreg Gwalch, 1995)

Williams, M., *The Slate Industry*, (Shire Publications, 1991)

Articles:

Tucker G. & M., *The Slate Industries of Pembrokeshire*, (Industrial Archaeology Review, 1979)

Tucker G. & M., *The Old Slate Industries of Pembrokeshire and other parts of South Wales*, (National Library of Wales Journal XXIII / 2 1983)

Thesis:

Industrial Development in a North Pembrokeshire rural

community during the nineteenth century. The slate quarrying settlement of Rosebush. (Shelagh M. Daniel MA UW, 1983)

Typescript Essay:
Tucker G. & M., *The Slate Industry in Pembrokeshire and Neighbouring Counties*. (CRO Haverfordwest)

Principal Collections Consulted:
Davies Porthmadog Collection, Glandovan papers, Glansevin Papers, Haverfordwest (Williams & Williams) Collection, Lucas Picton Estate Papers, (National Library Aberystwyth)
Dolbadau Account Books, John Williams Diaries, (CRO Haverfordwest)
Coedmore Collection, (CRO Carmarthen)
Tucker Deposit, (RCAHM Aberystwyth)

Newspapers:
Cambrian, Cardigan & Teifyside Advertiser, Dewsland & Kemes Guardian, Haverfordwest & Milford Haven Telegraph, Pembrokshire Herald, Western Telegraph

Trade Periodicals:
Quarry Manager's Journal, Mining Journal, Slate Trades Gazette

Acknowledgements

My thanks are due to:-
J.D. Absalom, Max Bowen, P. Brasswood, S. Mansel Davies, Victor Griffiths, Steve Martin, Bernard Morris, Dr Dafydd Roberts, Jeremy Wilkinson, Richard M. Williams, Roger Worsley and many others including the numerous landowners and occupiers who generously granted me access to their properties and records.

The ever helpful staffs of the Aberystwyth, Carmarthen, Caernarfon, Llandrindod Wells and Haverfordwest Record Offices, Carmarthen and Haverfordwest Libraries, Scolton Manor Museum, the National Library of Wales and the Royal Commission on Ancient and Historic Monuments, Aberystwyth.

And to my wife Delphine who constantly assists with both fieldwork and research.

Particular acknowledgement is made to the work of the late Professor Gordon and Mrs Mary Tucker whose notes, maps and plans, generously deposited at the Haverfordwest Record Office and the RCAHM Aberystwyth, have been such an invaluable guide to sources.

By the same author, published by Gwasg Carreg Gwalch:
A Gazeteer of the Welsh Slate Industry   ISBN: 0-86381-196-5
Slate Quarrying at Corris   ISBN: 0-86381-279-1
Slate Quarrying in Wales   ISBN: 0-86381-319-4

Industrial Archaeology & Railways

A Gazeteer of the Welsh Slate Industry
– Alun John Richards. Details and historical notes on 400+ quarries and mills in Wales representing 20 years of field work.
240 pp; ISBN 0-86381-196-5; **£6.90**

Slate Quarrying in Wales
– Alun John Richards. From its earliest beginnings to the present day, this book follows the fortunes and misfortunes of this great industry.
231 pp; ISBN 0-86381-319-4; **£7.50**

Slate Quarrying in Corris
– Alun John Richards. First detailed account of the area.
144 pp; ISBN 0-86381-279-1; **£5.45**

Delving in Dinorwig
– Douglas C. Carrington. First detailed account of a fascinating slate quarry.
ISBN 0-86381-285-6; **£7.50**

The Golden Age of Brymbo Steam
– Geoff and Hugh Charles. Old photographs and memories of the Brymbo railway lines. ISBN 0-86381-435-2; **£5.75**

Three Stops to the Summit
– Rol Williams. The history of the Snowdon Mountain Railway.
ISBN 0-86381-433-6; **£4.95**

Historic Landscapes of the Great Orme
– Mary Aris. Early agriculture and copper-mining – a new persepctive on Llandudno's landscape and history. 114 pages quarto; maps; diagrams; illustrations; ISBN 0-86381-357-7; **£7.95**

The Llŷn Peninsula Mines
– Wil Williams. A history of manganese mining on the peninsula; 64 pages; bilingual; illustrations. ISBN 0-86381-315-1; **£3**

New for 1998:
The Slate Quarries of Pembrokeshire
– Alun John Richards. Including illustrations & maps.
ISBN 0-86381-484-0; **£5.50**

Welsh Heritage Series

An informative series of books full of interesting facts and illustrations, presenting Wales, its history, its folklore, its character and its language.

1 Shrouded Quays (Lost Ports of Wales)
– Aled Eames. 96 pp; ISBN 0-86381-197-3; many illustrations; **£2.50**

2 Welsh Pub Names
– Myrddin ap Dafydd. 84 pp ISBN 0-86481-185-X; many illustrations; **£2.50**

3 Traditional Fishing in Wales
– Emrys Evans. 72 pp; ISBN 0-86381-320-8; many illustrations; **£3.50**

4 A History of the Red Dragon
– Carl Lofmark. The national symbol of Wales through the ages. ISBN 0-86381-317-8; **£3.50**

5 A Guide to Welsh Place-Names
– Anthony Lias. ISBN 0-86381-289-9; **£3.50**

NEW FOR 1998:

6 The Herring Fishers of Wales
– Mike Smylie. A journey, following the 'silver darlings' along the coast of Wales, calling at the different ports and small harbours, retelling the history of the herring fisheries in Wales. 128 pp; ISBN 0-86381-467-0; **£3.75**

7 A Study of Radnorshire Place-names
– Richard Morgan. 96 pp; ISBN 0-86381-475-1; **£4.50**

8 Welsh Nots, Welsh Notes and Welsh Nuts
A dictionary of phrases using the word 'Welsh' by T.B. Edwards. ISBN 0-86381-485-9; **£4.75**

Welsh Cooking and Cafés

Welsh Country Cooking
– Chris Grant. A selection of traditional and well-loved recipies. 72 pp; ISBN 0-86381-261-9; spiral binding; **£3.00**

The Smallest House Cook Book
– Margaret Williams. The 'smallest house' is at Conwy and these recipies are full of the fruits of the land, the sea and the river. 48 pp; ISBN 0-86381-223-6; **£1.95**

The Teatime Guide
– Dewi and Pamela Roberts. 48 afternoon tea venues in North Wales. 64 pp ISBN 0-86381-342-9; **£3.00**

Mountaineering & Botany

The Complete Guide to Snowdon/Yr Wyddfa
– Robert Joes. PVC Cover; ISBN 0-86381-222-8; **£6.95**

The Lakes of Eryri
– Geraint Roberts. Wildlife, fishing and folklore enhances this book aimed at anyone who loves Snowdonia. PVC cover; 256 pp; ISBN 0-86381-338-0; **£8.90**

The Mountain Walker's Guide to Wales
– Colin Adams. A comprehensive guide to 100 routes covering 200 Welsh peaks. 192 pp; ISBN 0-86381-154-X; Map, PVC Cover; **£6.90**

The Botanists and Guides of Snowdonia
– Dewi Jones. An account of the local guides and the plant hunters. 172 pp; ISBN 0-86381-383-6; **£6.95**

Travellers in Wales

Visitor's Delight
– Dewi Roberts. An anthology of visitor's impressions of North Wales. 152 pp; ISBN 0-86381-224-4; **£3.75**

The A-Z of Betws-y-coed
– Donald Shaw. Full of facts, stories and history about the popular Welsh resort. 136 pp; 0-86381-153-1; **£2.99**

Snowdonia, A Historical Anthology
– David Kirk. 60 writers portray the people and landscape of one of the most beautiful regions in Europe. 248 pp; ISBN 0-86381-270-8; **£5.95**

All the Days were Glorious
– Gwyn Neale. George Gissing in North Wales – quotes from Gissing's letters and diary. 56 pp; ISBN 0-86381-286-4; **£2.95**

The Land of Old Renown – George Borrow in Wales
– Dewi Roberts. A retrace of George Borrow's journey through Wales. ISBN 0-86381-436-0; **£4.50**

Both Sides of the Border
An Anthology of writing on the Welsh Border Region by Dewi Roberts. ISBN 0-86381-461-1; **£4.75**

A Tour in Wales by Thomas Pennant
An old classic abridged by David Kirk. 176 pp; ISBN 0-86381-473-5; **£5.75**

Revd John Parker's Tour of Wales and its Churches (1798-1860)
Abridged by Edgar W. Parry. ISBN 0-86381-481-6; **£4.75**